D A V I D   B O O T H

STORIES TO READ ALOUD

Pembroke Publishers Limited

For Bill Halloran

© 1992 Pembroke Publishers
538 Hood Road
Markham, Ontario L3R 3K9

Canadian Cataloguing in Publication Data

Main entry under title:

Stories to read aloud

Includes bibliographical references.
ISBN 0-921217-89-7

1. Children's stories, Canadian (English).*
2. Children's stories, American. 3. Children's
stories, English. 4. Children's stories, Canadian
(English) – Study and teaching.* 5. Children's
stories, American – Study and teaching.
6. Children's stories, English – Study and
teaching. I. Booth, David W. (David Wallace),
1938-   .

PS8329.S78 1992   C813'.54   C92-094772-7
PR9197.32.S78 1992

Editor: David Kilgour
Design: John Zehethofer
Cover Illustration: Graham Pilsworth
Typesetting: Jay Tee Graphics Ltd.

This book was produced with the generous assistance of the government
of Ontario through the Ministry of Culture and Communications.

Printed and bound in Canada
9 8 7 6 5 4 3 2

Contents

Introduction

The first time I read aloud to a group of children, a small boy wandered over to the classroom typewriter and began pecking away at the keys. As a young consultant demonstrating the strategy of sharing stories to teachers, I was forced to decide whether to stop the story, stop the typing or go on with the story as if I were unaware of the disruption. By some lucky stroke of fate, I chose the third option, and when the sense of story filled the room, the miscreant returned to the group and entered the tale. Now, with my collected wisdom of some thirty years of reading aloud, I am still sometimes faced with similar problems, and my choice in dealing with them depends on a thousand variables, but my constant belief in the power of story remains strong and true.

In today's educational milieus, reading to children is a highly prized activity. No longer do we flinch when the principal walks into our classroom and finds us in the middle of sharing a powerful selection from the myriad of choices that contemporary literature for young people offers us. Mothers, fathers, teachers, older siblings — all are part of the read-aloud network, and children of all ages snuggle on the couch, gather on the rug, sit around the table or nestle in their beds, to experience that most ordinary and fabulous of all constructs — the story.

As adults, we can bring them stories that they can't handle on their own, that they might not choose, that at first seem outside their range of experience of print. Children can step outside their own culture, their past lives, their experiences, into other worlds — strange, different, unsettling or fantastic — meet characters that they didn't know existed or that stare back from the mirror. They can be transported into story worlds with no fear of word recognition or word attack — in reading aloud, story is all, meaning is everything. The deepest issues can be explored, argued, clarified, wondered about. We are all part of the story experience, irrespective of our stage of reading development or our knowledge of comprehension strategies. The story's voice speaks to all of us.

The story tribe creates an atmosphere conducive to print and text. We all are in the circle, waiting for the moment when we step through the mirror, chant the hidden ritual, find the golden key. We talk about the story, the author, the times, the characters, the connections, the concepts that touch and affect us. We know story; we are story. We will read stories and write them as a normal part of school, of life, of being literate. In doing so, we demonstrate our new possibilities as members of our literate community.

Listening to books read aloud provokes children into entering the world of the reader, and heightens their curiosity about this phenomenon and about their own desire to find out how they can become members of this literacy club.

Children become interested in print when they are immersed in listening to books read aloud. Teachers can read aloud throughout the day, every day — favorite stories, stories on a theme, stories by the same author or illustrator, stories with similar patterns and structures, stories connected to each other.

Research indicates a strong connection between a child's success in reading and awareness of stories and poems, along with the knowledge of how books work. Reading aloud to children promotes a love of literature, an understanding of story patterns, sentence structures and word power. Language learning is an integrated process: listening to literature opens children to new experiences, different language strategies, exciting images and metaphors.

As the reader brings the words to life, listeners create pictures in their minds and imaginations, shadows to give background to future literacy experiences, to build the frames for meaning-making.

What stories have I chosen for this book? There is only room for a few, in a world of thousands. Each selection, then, must represent others and yet be its own literary experience. I began by selecting my favorites, and then looking for patterns behind their success with the children with whom I had shared them. One author can conjure up a dozen successful stories for reading aloud. Tall tales form their own networks, and retellers and anthologists are there to support us.

Stories that I enjoy reading again and again draw upon the story bones of folklore. Tales that are told and retold obviously have a special power, and I can tap into these archetypal versions from other times and share them with today's story tribe. In this collection, you will find tall tales from Appalachia, legends from Ireland, fairy tales from England, folktales from the Caribbean, besides new variations by contemporary writers, who borrow the patterns from the past as frames for their tellings.

I look for stories that contain universal truths that we can all recognize, inside a narrative that will hold the attention of a group of youngsters from various backgrounds. Because of the different ages and stages of children in the groups with whom I work, the stories need to speak to a wide audience, and I search for tales that accommodate a range of responses in their retellings, so that most children can find the story they need inside the story frame I read. With very young children, I may need to pause during the story so that they can express some stirring emotion, or clarify a problem or even ease tension.

Of course, all stories are shape shifters, depending upon the experience. For example, the style of reading can alter the mood of listeners. Depending on whether I gather them around me, or speak from a stage, or use a microphone, then the story itself takes on different shapes and shadows. If I use a dramatic interpretation of the dialogue, or a whisper for the narration, then the atmosphere alters. Some stories allow the audience to join in, to respond as a chorus. Others demand a deep silence so that they can be reflected upon. I have never worried about having an untrained voice in my reading aloud, for children will forgive us our weaknesses if the story is strong and significant. Perhaps it is best if the reader begins to disappear as the story takes on a life of its own.

I have taped stories as rehearsal, and I have tried completely different interpretations on a series of classes. The ultimate goal is to sound as if you are reading a story for the first time, yet to read it as if you have always known it. For me, the focus of the experience is vital: I try to ignore all extraneous goings-on, and to create a sense of theatrical intimacy with the group. Their attention span may depend upon the story, but other pressures can affect their listening as well, from an imminent recess period to a story with no appropriate connections to their lives.

Each time I read a story, I find new points to work on, words I have skipped over, nuances in lines that emerge as my comfort level increases. The audience's response affects my reading each time, demanding that I slow down, speed up or add significant pauses. The words themselves become part of my own speech as I reread, and I can begin to jiggle and juggle them to find the right emphasis, an effective rhythm or sense of the sounds of the story as well as its inner sense. Often illustrations help, as the children both watch and listen as the story unfolds.

In the course of putting together this collection, I found stories that connect to other stories, that resonate with our own experiences — twists and turns in a well-known plot, themes like daring to challenge fate, struggling with seemingly hopeless odds, facing our private and darkest fears.

You will find a short list of story sets at the end of this book, and you can add your own to build a web to catch everyone. Developing a repertoire takes time, and this book may begin your collection. Try the stories, adapt them, discard them, try them again. Different audiences, moods, settings, and prior experiences can affect the response to a story. But begin with the stories here and let the children take you to the next story set. Treasure the stories you find, and share them with others.

Perhaps we shouldn't choose books children select for themselves, unless they are common favorites we all want to celebrate one more time. Usually, I choose a story that will interest children and stretch them in some way. It might be part of their current curriculum theme, or it might fit the mood of the moment, or it might stimulate interest in an author's other works. Perhaps a balance should be attempted that reflects the variety of stories available to children alongside those types of tales the children know and enjoy.

At times I read several short stories; at other times, I share longer, continuous stories. The story tribe is a special group — some stories work for all ages; some have particular relevance for different groups — children with different backgrounds, different book experiences, different sensibilities. Choosing appropriate books for specific groups of children is an art that grows with practice and experience. That is why you won't find any specific guidelines about appropriate age levels or targeted audiences for the stories in this book: you know your students best, and you should trust your instincts about what stories will work best for them — even if that means making a few mistakes. I myself often make mistakes in choosing an appropriate selection for a group of children — it may be too removed from their lives, too old or too young a telling, too funny or too serious, too real or too unreal. And yet, if you know the children, the choice is much more easily made. My work has largely been with new audiences each time, in demonstration situations, and therefore I have relied on the story to take hold of the listeners in these strange circumstances, and I have grown fond of those authors who seem to write specifically for my needs. When I am searching for a new book at my favorite children's book store, or on the shelf of new books at the library, the sight of a recognized and trusted author offers a starting point for selection. Of course, the new story has to be run through, tested, tried out, accepted or rejected. I read dozens to find the one I want, and I still favor some I have used for thirty-five years.

The selections in this collection represent the authors and collectors of stories that have supported my read-aloud ventures with many audiences, from my own son to three thousand children in a sports arena. I trust that you will add these story artists to your own list of special people, and seek out other selections by them to add to your repertoire of stories to read aloud. Some of these stories revisit old tales retold or adapted, while others borrow patterns from long ago. But all are stamped with the artistry of the writer, if only by the genius of the locating and selecting of a story that takes the audience by the throat or the heart or the soul. I choose to read these aloud because the words matter, the order of the words matters. I become the voice, the interpreter, the medium that breathes life into print, and yet it must be the story that the children experience, not me.

I have to like a story if I am to read it to a group of children. It must be a story I enjoy reading aloud, since I am adding it to my story repertoire. A story that works for one teacher (or one class) may not have the same effect on another teacher (or class). Some stories are most effective when read to a small, intimate group; others are better with larger audiences.

A story (or group of stories) represents a special event for me. I want to make the most of the experience. Sometimes I prepare an introduction for a book to set the time or place or mood. Other times, I select a story to fit inside an already existing learning web. Often, I work with the class after the story, extending and exploring the issues inside and outside it. The community of learners can benefit greatly from this shared literary experience, the learning can continue in a thousand ways, as children role-play incidents, storytell sections, discuss questions and problems, read sections aloud, write about personal responses, draw and paint and graph all types of reactions. A good story is a complete learning package. We must remember that reading a story aloud to a group of children is, in a sense, a performance, where the audience gathers together to focus on the story reader and the story. Unlike watching television or film, there is an immediacy in reading a story aloud that draws the energies of everyone into the moment. This gives us as teachers a powerful tool for involving active minds and imaginations through the strength of story.

How many read-aloud experiences can you create for children? There are countless possibilities:

- rereading a story the whole class loves;
- reading their own choices;
- playing recordings of authors and artists reading stories;
- having retired volunteers share books with young audiences;
- having older students read to younger buddies;
- having groups of students prepare a story for an audience of their peers;
- having singers and musicians share a story-song connected to a theme;
- reading a story as a monologue where you take on the persona of a character;
- finding a new version of a well-known story;
- sharing a brand-new book by an admired author or illustrator;
- reading a book by an author you have met or read about;
- reading a story that requires the help of the listening audience to come alive;
- reading under a tree in the playground on a hot June afternoon.

And the list goes on. I don't know why children listen to stories, but they almost always do. I sit on a chair, they squat on a rug, and we become one with the tale. They look at me, but see no one. I read the words, and they hear a dozen voices. I know the story well, and yet I have never heard it before. We are the story tribe. We always have been. We always will be.

OWL

DIANE WOLKSTEIN

(Reading time: 6 minutes)

"Owl" is a Haitian tale from The Magic Orange Tree, *collected by Diane Wolkstein, the well-known storyteller, on a trip to Haiti, where she first heard an islander tell it to a crowd near Port-au-Prince. It is an unusual and arresting tale, of love and deceit, with a rhythmic drive that includes a dancing refrain.*

I enjoy reading this to listeners of all ages; its characters — Owl and Rooster — draw in the youngest children, while its theme of unrequited love affects even the most cynical youth.

Over the years, I have heard several storytellers present their versions, each one in different form, from jubilant song to dance. But for me, the theme is one of tentative and passionate adolescents, meeting love face to face, and the ending reflects the complexities of the choices we make in our lives.

Owl thought he was very ugly. But one evening he met a girl and talked with her and she liked him. "If it had been day," Owl thought, "and she had seen my face, she never would have liked me." But still she had liked him.

So Owl went to her house the next night. And the next. And the night after that. Every evening he would arrive at the girl's house at seven, and they would sit outside on the porch steps, talking together politely.

Then one evening after Owl had left, the girl's mother said to her, "Why doesn't your fiancé come and visit you during the day?"

"But Mama, he's explained that to me. He works during the day. Then he must go home and change and he cannot get here before seven."

"Still, I would like to see his face before the marriage," the mother said. "Let's invite him to our house for a dance this

Sunday afternoon. Surely he doesn't work on Sunday."

Owl was very pleased with the invitation: a dance in his honor. But he was also very frightened. He told his cousin, Rooster, about the girl and asked him to accompany him to the dance. But that Sunday afternoon, as Owl and Rooster were riding on their horses to the dance, Owl glanced over at Rooster. Rooster held himself with such assurance, he was so elegantly and fashionably dressed, that Owl imagined the girl seeing the two of them and was filled with shame.

"I can't go on," he choked. "You go and tell them I've had an accident and will be there later."

Rooster rode to the dance. "Tsk tsk, poor Owl," he explained. "He has had an accident, and he has asked me to let you know that he will be here later."

When it was quite dark, Owl tied his horse a good distance from the dance and stumbled up to the porch steps.

"Pssst," he whispered to a young man sitting on the steps. "Is Rooster here?"

"Well now, I don't know."

"Go and look. Tell him a friend is waiting for him by the mapou* tree."

Rooster came out. "OWL!"

"Shhhhhh—"

"*Owl!*"

"Shhh—"

"Owl, what are you wearing over your head — I mean your face?"

"It's a hat. Haven't you ever seen a hat before? Look, tell them anything. Tell them I scratched my eyes on a branch as I was riding here and the light — even the light from a lamp — hurts them. And you must be certain to watch for the day for me, and to crow as soon as you see the light, so we can leave."

"Yes, yes," Rooster said. "Come in and I shall introduce you to the girl's relatives."

Rooster introduced Owl to everyone, explaining Owl's predicament. Owl went around shaking hands, his hat hung down almost completely covering his face. Owl then tried to retreat into a corner, but the girl came over.

"Come into the yard and let's dance," she said.

---

* *mapou* (pronounced ma-pu) is believed in Haiti to be inhabited by evil spirits.

Dong ga da, Dong ga da, Dong ga da, Dong.
Dong ga da, Dong. Eh-ee-oh.

Owl danced. And Owl could dance well. The girl was proud of Owl. Even if he wore his hat strangely and had sensitive eyes, he *could* dance.

Dong ga da, Dong ga da, Dong ga da, Dong.
Donga ga da, Dong. Eh-ee-oh.

Rooster was dancing too. When Owl noticed that Rooster was dancing, instead of watching for the day, Owl was afraid that Rooster would forget to warn him, and he excused himself to the girl. He ran out to the yard, past the houses to a clearing where he could see the horizon. No, it was still night. Owl came back.

Dong ga da, Dong ga da, Dong ga da, Dong.
Dong ga da, Dong. Eh-ee-oh.

Owl motioned to Rooster, but Rooster was lost in the dance. Owl excused himself again to the girl, ran to the clearing; no, it was still night. Owl returned.

Dong ga da, Dong ga da, Dong ga da, Dong.
Dong ga da, Dong. Eh-ee-oh.

Owl tried to excuse himself again, but the girl held on to him. "Yes, stay with me," she said. And so they danced and danced and danced.

Dong ga da, Dong ga da, Dong ga da, Dong.
Dong ga da, Dong. Eh-ee-oh.

The sun moved up in the sky, higher and higher, until it filled the house and the yard with light.
"Now — let us see your fiancé's face!" the mother said.
"*Kokioko!*"* Rooster crowed.
And before Owl could hide, she reached out and pulled the hat from his face.
"MY EYES!" Owl cried, and covering his face with his hands, he ran for his horse.
"Wait, Owl!" the girl called.
"*Kokioko!*" Rooster crowed.

* *Kokioko* (Ko-kee-o-ko) is Creole for cock-a-doodle-doo.

"Wait, Owl, wait."

And as Owl put his hands down to untie his horse, the girl saw his face. It was striking and fierece, and the girl thought it was the most handsome face she had ever seen.

"Owl —"

But Owl was already on his horse, riding away, farther and farther away.

Owl never came back.

The girl waited. Then she married Rooster. She was happy, except sometimes in the morning when Rooster would crow "kokioko-o-o." Then she would think about Owl and wonder where he was.

Wiley and the Hairy Man

VIRGINIA HAVILAND

(Reading time: 10 minutes)

"Wiley and the Hairy Man" is a popular tale found in many folklore anthologies. Virginia Haviland included it in her representative anthology, The Faber Book of North American Legends, *as an example of African-American conjure tales, in which the weak triumph over the strong, with the help of "conjuration", whereby a medicine man or woman works magic through the use of charms.*

This is a favorite story of mine to read aloud to all ages. It has rich opportunities for vocal dramatization, and a narrative of true suspense. If the dialect is a problem, let the rhythm of the language assist you.

Wiley's pappy was a bad man and no-count. He stole watermelons in the dark of the moon. He was lazy, too, and slept while the weeds grew higher than the cotton. Worse still, he killed three martins and never even chunked at a crow.

One day he fell off the ferry boat where the river is quicker than anywhere else and no one ever found him. They looked for him a long way down river and in the still pools between the sand-banks, but they never found him. They heard a big man laughing across the river, and everybody said, "That's the Hairy Man." So they stopped looking.

"Wiley," his mammy told him, "the Hairy Man's got your pappy and he's goin' to get you if you don't look out."

"Yas'm," he said. "I'll look out. I'll take my hound-dogs everywhere I go. The Hairy Man can't stand no hound-dog."

Wiley knew that because his mammy had told him. She knew because she came from the swamps by the Tombisbee River and knew conjure magic.

One day Wiley took his axe and went down in the swamp to cut some poles for a hen-roost and his hounds went with him. But they took out after a shoat* and ran it so far off Wiley couldn't even hear them yelp.

"Well," he said, "I hope the Hairy Man ain't nowhere round here now."

He picked up his axe to start cutting poles, but he looked up and there came the Hairy Man through the trees grinning. He was sure ugly and his grin didn't help much. He was hairy all over. His eyes burned like fire and spit drooled all over his big teeth.

"Don't look at me like that," said Wiley, but the Hairy Man kept coming and grinning, so Wiley threw down his axe and climbed up a big bay tree. He saw the Hairy Man didn't have feet like a man but like a cow, and Wiley never had seen a cow up a bay tree.

"What for you done climb up there?" the Hairy Man asked Wiley when he got to the bottom of the tree.

Wiley climbed nearly to the top of the tree and looked down. Then he climbed plumb to the top.

"How come you climbin' trees?" the Hairy Man said.

"My mammy done tole me to stay away from you. What you got in that big croaker-sack†?"

"I ain't got nothin' yet."

"Gwan away from here," said Wiley, hoping the tree would grow some more.

"Ha," said the Hairy Man and picked up Wiley's axe. He swung it about and the chips flew. Wiley grabbed the tree close, rubbed his belly on it and hollered, "Fly, chips, fly, back in your same old place."

The chips flew and the Hairy Man cussed and damned. Then he swung the axe and Wiley knew he'd have to holler fast. They went to it tooth and toe-nail then, Wiley hollering and the Hairy Man chopping. He hollered till he was hoarse and he saw the Hairy Man was gaining on him.

"I'll come down part of the way," he said, "if you'll make this bay tree twice as big around."

"I ain't studyin' you," said the Hairy Man, swinging the axe.

"I bet you can't," said Wiley.

"I ain't going to try," said the Hairy Man.

* young pig
† a sack for gathering frogs

Then they went to it again, Wiley hollering and the Hairy Man chopping. Wiley had about yelled himself out when he heard his hound-dogs yelping way off.

"Hyeaaah, dog," hollered Wiley, and then both heard the houng-dogs yelping and coming jam-up. The Hairy Man looked worried.

"Come on down," he said, "and I'll teach you conjure."

"I can learn all the conjure I want from my mammy."

The Hairy Man cussed some more, but he threw the axe down and took off through the swamp.

When Wiley got home he told his mammy that the Hairy Man had most got him, but his dogs ran him off.

"Did he have his sack?"

"Yas'm."

"Next time he come after you, don't you climb no bay tree."

"I ain't," said Wiley. "They ain't big enough around."

"Don't climb no kind ' tree. Just stay on the ground and say 'Hello, Hairy Man.' You hear me, Wiley?"

"No'm."

"He ain't goin' to hurt you, child. You can put the Hairy Man in the dirt when I tell you how to do him."

"I puts him in the dirt and he puts me in that croaker-sack. I ain't puttin' no Hairy Man in the dirt."

"You just do like I say. You say, 'Hello, Hairy Man.' He says, 'Hello, Wiley,' You say, 'Hairy Man, I done heard you about the best conjureman round here.' 'I reckon I am.' You say, 'I bet you cain't turn yourself into no giraffe.' You keep tellin' him he cain't and he will. Then you say, 'I bet you cain't turn yourself into no 'possum.' Then he will, and you grab him and throw him in the sack."

"It don't sound just right somehow," said Wiley, "but I will." So he tied up his dogs so they wouldn't scare away the Hairy Man, and went down to the swamp again. He hadn't been there long when he looked up and there came the Hairy Man grinning through the trees, hairy all over and his big teeth showing more than ever. He knew Wiley came off without his hound-dogs. Wiley nearly climbed a tree when he saw the croaker-sack, but he didn't.

"Hello, Hairy Man," he said.

"Hello, Wiley." He took the sack off his shoulder and started opening it up.

"Hairy Man, I done heard you are about the best conjure man round here."

"I reckon I is."

"I bet you cain't turn yourself into no giraffe."

"Shucks, that ain't no trouble," said the Hairy Man.

"I bet you cain't do it."

So the Hairy Man twisted round and turned himself into a giraffe.

"I bet you cain't turn yourself into no alligator," said Wiley.

The giraffe twisted around and turned into an alligator, all the time watching Wiley to see he didn't try to run.

"Anybody can turn theyself into something big as a man," said Wiley, "but I bet you cain't turn yourself into no 'possum."

The alligator twisted around and turned into a 'possum, and Wiley grabbed it and threw it in the sack.

Wiley tied the sack up as tight as he could and then he threw it in the river. He started home through the swamp and he looked up and there came the Hairy Man grinning through the trees. Wiley had to scramble up the nearest tree.

The Hairy Man gloated: "I turned myself into the wind and blew out. Wiley, I'm going to set right here till you get hungry and fall out of that bay tree. You want me to learn you some more conjure?"

Wiley studied a while. He studied the Hairy Man and he studied about his hound-dogs tied up most a mile away.

"Well," he said, "you done some pretty smart tricks. But I bet you cain't make things disappear and go where nobody knows."

"Huh, that's what I'm good at. Look at that old bird-nest on the limb. Now look. It's done gone."

"How I know it was there in the first place? I bet you cain't make something I know is there disappear."

"Ha ha!" said the Hairy Man. "Look at your shirt."

Wiley looked down and his shirt was gone, but he didn't care, because that was just what he wanted the Hairy Man to do.

"That was just a plain old shirt," he said. "But this rope I got tied round my breeches has been conjured. I bet you cain't make it disappear."

"Huh, I can make all the rope in this county disappear."

"Ha ha ha," said Wiley.

The Hairy Man looked mad and threw his chest way out. He

opened his mouth wide and hollered loud.

"From now on all the rope in this county has done disappeared."

Wiley reared back, holding his breeches with one hand and a tree-limb with the other.

"Hyeaaah, dog," he hollered loud enough to be heard more than a mile off.

When Wiley and his dogs got back home his mammy asked him did he put the Hairy Man in the sack.

"Yes'm, but he done turned himself into the wind and blew right through that old croaker-sack."

"That *is* bad," said his mammy. "But you done fool him twice. If you fool him again he'll leave you alone. He'll be mighty hard to fool the third time."

"We got to study up a way to fool him, mammy."

"I'll study up a way tereckly," she said, and sat down by the fire and held her chin between her hands and studied real hard. But Wiley wasn't studying anything except how to keep the Hairy Man away. He took his hound-dogs out and tied one at the back door and one at the front door. Then he crossed a broom and an axe-handle over the window and built a fire in the fire-place. Feeling a lot safer, he sat down and helped his mammy study. After a little while his mammy said, "Wiley, you go down to the pen and get that little suckin' pig away from that old sow."

Wiley went down and snatched the sucking pig through the rails and left the sow grunting and heaving in the pen. He took the pig back to his mammy and she put it in his bed.

"Now, Wiley," she said, "you go on up to the loft and hide."

So he did. Before long he heard the wind howling and the trees shaking, and then his dogs started growling. He looked out through a knot-hole in the planks and saw the dog at the front door looking down toward the swamps, with his hair standing up and his lips drawn back in a snarl. Then an animal as big as a mule with horns on its head ran out of the swamp past the house. The dog jerked and jumped, but he couldn't get loose. Then an animal bigger than a great big dog with a long nose and big teeth ran out of the swamp and growled at the cabin. This time the dog broke loose and took after the big animal, who ran back down into the swamp. Wiley looked out another chink at the back end of the loft just in time to see his other dog jerk loose and take out after an animal which might have been a 'possum, but wasn't.

"Law-dee," said Wiley. "The Hairy Man is coming here, sure."

He didn't have long to wait, because soon enough he heard something with feet like a cow scrambling around on the roof. He knew it was the Hairy Man, because he heard him swear when he touched the hot chimney. The Hairy Man jumped off the roof when he found out there was a fire in the fire-place and came up and knocked on the front door as big as you please.

"Mammy," he hollered, "I done come after your baby."

"You ain't going to get him," mammy hollered back.

"Give him here or I'll set your house on fire with lightning."

"I got plenty of sweet-milk to put it out with."

"Give him here or I'll dry up your spring, make your cow go dry and send a million boll-weevils out of the ground to eat up your cotton."

"Hairy Man, you wouldn't do all that. That's mighty mean."

"I'm a mighty mean man. I ain't never seen a man as mean as I am."

"If I give you my baby will you go on way from here and leave everything else alone?"

"I swear that's just what I'll do," said the Hairy Man, so mammy opened the door and let him in.

"He's over there in that bed," she said.

The Hairy Man came in grinning like he was meaner than he said. He walked over to the bed and snatched the covers back.

"Hey," he hollered, "there ain't nothing in this bed but a old suckin' pig."

"I ain't said what kind of baby I was giving you, and that suckin' pig sure belong to me before I gave it to you."

The Hairy Man raged and yelled. He stomped all over the house gnashing his teeth. Then he grabbed up the pig and tore out through the swamp, knocking down trees right and left. The next morning the swamp had a wide path like a cyclone had cut through it, with trees torn loose at the roots and lying on the ground. When the Hairy Man was gone Wiley came down from the loft.

"Is he done gone, mammy?"

"Yes, child. That old Hairy Man cain't ever hurt you again. We done fool him three times."

The Porcelain Man

RICHARD KENNEDY

(Reading time: 6 minutes)

I first read "The Porcelain Man" as a picture book, and when I subsequently found it in Richard Kennedy: Collected Stories, *I realized that it was part of a significant body of work by a fine American writer.*

This is a startling story of loneliness and love, in which the author takes us into a fantasy that results in our seeing deeper into the human heart. A lonely girl living with her nasty father comes to build a man of porcelain, who tells her that he loves her. The twists and turns will surprise audiences of every age into realizing the difficulty of living with our choices in life.

Once upon a time at the edge of town lived a harsh man with a timid daughter who had grown pale and dreamy from too much obedience. The man kept the girl busy and hardly ever let her go out of doors. "You're lucky to be inside where it's safe and sound," he would say to her. "It's dog-eat-dog out there. The world is full of bottle-snatchers, ragmongers and ratrobbers. Believe you me!"

The girl believed him.

Each morning the man left the house in his rickety wagon pulled by his rackety horse. All day long he would go up and down the streets of the town, into the countryside and to neighboring villages to find what he could find. He would bring home old broken wheels, tables and chairs with the legs gone from them, pots and pans with holes in them, scraps of this and pieces of that. His daughter would then mend and repair the junk during her long and lonely days inside the house, and the man would take the things away and sell them as secondhand goods. This is the way they lived.

One morning the man left the house and gave his daughter his usual instruction and warning. "If someone passes on the road, stay away from the windows. If someone knocks, don't answer. I could tell you terrible stories." Then he left, and the girl began work on a broken lantern.

Now this morning some good luck happened to the man. As he was passing a rich man's house, a clumsy kitchen maid chased two cats out the front door with a broom and knocked over a large porcelain vase. The vase rolled out the door and down the steps and path, and shattered to pieces against a marble pillar near the roadway. The man stopped and watched. The maid closed the door. The man waited there for ten minutes. No one came out. Then he leaped down from his cart and gathered up the broken porcelain. He set the pieces gently in his cart and hurried off toward home.

His daughter, as usual, was safe and sound inside. "This is fine porcelain," the man said. "Drop whatever you're doing and patch it up. We'll get a good price for it."

It was early in the day yet, so the man left again to see what else he might find. He remembered to pause at the door and say, "Stay inside. Terrible things are going on out there. Dog-eat-dog, the devil take the hindmost, and so forth." Then he left.

The girl turned a piece of porcelain in her fingers, admiring its beauty. She carefully laid the pieces on a blanket and got out the glue. Then, humming to herself and musing on fanciful thoughts in the way she had acquired from being so much alone, she began to put the pieces of porcelain together. She worked quickly and neatly even though her thoughts were completely elsewhere, and at the end of a couple of hours she was amazed to see that she had just set the last piece in place on a full-sized porcelain man. And at that moment the porcelain man spoke.

"I love you," he said, taking a step toward the girl.

"Gracious!" gasped the girl, snatching up the blanket and throwing it about the man. "Gracious!" she gasped again as the porcelain man encircled her in his arms and kissed her.

While this was happening, the girl's father returned to the house. And right at this moment he opened the door to the room.

"Whoa!" he bellowed.

He grabbed a chair, raised it above his head and brought it down squarely on top of the head of the porcelain man with a blow that shattered him from head to toe, and the porcelain pieces scattered over the floor.

"Godamighty!" the man cried, "I've fractured his skull!" The girl let out a wail, and the man dropped to his knees, stunned with the catastrophe. But the girl explained that it had not been a real man, but only one made of the porcelain.

"A porcelain man who could move!?"

"And he could talk as well," said the girl.

"Fantastic!" said the man. "Quick, put him together again before you forget how you did it. I'll make a cage for him and take him to the county fair. I'll charge a dollar to see him. He can learn to dance. I'll make a big sign saying, 'See the dancing pot,' or something like that. I'll make thousands! Quick, put him together again!"

So the girl collected the pieces on the blanket and slowly began gluing them together again. Her father sat down and watched her for a while, but he found it to be boring and he dropped off to sleep.

The girl worked on, very sad that the porcelain man would be taken away in a cage. She was so distressed by her thoughts that she did not notice until putting the last piece in place that she had built a small porcelain horse. And the horse neighed.

The man woke up.

"What's that?" he said. "That's no man, that's a horse. Now you'll just have to do it all over again. And this time, *concentrate*!" Saying this, the man took up the chair over his head so as to smash the horse.

But the horse said to the girl, "Quickly, jump on my back!" She did, and in a second the horse leaped out the window with the girl, and they galloped across the countryside as the man stood waving the chair at them through the window and shouting words they could not hear.

After running for several miles, the horse stopped in a small meadow, in the centre of which stood a tree.

"Get down," said the horse. The girl did. "Now," said the horse, "I will run into the tree and break myself to pieces, and then you are to put me back together as a man again." Then the horse added, "Remember — I love you," and before the girl could say a word, the horse dashed toward the tree and crashed into it at full gallop and broke into hundreds of pieces.

The girl cried out, and then sat down under the tree and wept, for she had no glue.

Now on a path nearby came along a young man pushing a

wheelbarrow. He stopped when he saw the girl by the tree, and went to comfort her.

"Don't cry," he said. "Here, let us gather up the pieces and put them in the wheelbarrow. Come along with me and we'll fix everything almost as good as new."

So they loaded up the broken porcelain, and they went to the man's cottage and spread the pieces out on a blanket.

"It must have been a beautiful set of dishes," said the man, and he began to glue some pieces together. They talked as they worked and told each other all about themselves. The girl admired how well and how quickly the young man worked with his hands, and in a short while they had put together a dozen dishes, eight saucers and teacups, six bowls, two large serving platters, a milk pitcher, and two small vases.

They cooked supper then. Their eyes met often as they moved about. Now and again their hands touched, and they brushed against each other going to and fro.

They set the table with the porcelain ware, and when they were eating, the girl's plate whispered up at her, "I still love you."

"Hush!" she said.

"I beg your pardon?" the young man said.

"Oh, nothing," said the girl.

And they lived happily ever after.

Gallymanders! Gallymanders!

RICHARD CHASE

(Reading time: 10 minutes)

Richard Chase collected his stories from storytellers in the Appalachian communities in North Carolina and Virginia. "Gallymanders! Gallymanders!" is from his anthology, Grandfather Tales, *published over forty years ago and still popular today. Chase is a true folklorist, and he captures brilliantly the voices of the people who loved these tales.*

This story reflects its heritage in the fairy tales of the British Isles, but it has its own character, as you will find in the fun-filled manner in which the style draws you in, so that you will gallop along with the words as you chant:

> *"Seen a little gal go by here,*
> *with a jig and a jag*
> *and a long leather bag*
> *and all my gold and silver?"*

One time there was a stingy old woman lived all by herself. So stingy she didn't eat nothin' but ashcakes and water. Well, she was gettin' old and she had to have somebody to help her with the housework and all, so she sent across the water and hired her a girl. Now this girl she was mean, lazy, worked just enough to get around the old woman. Didn't care how she made up the beds, didn't half wash the dishes, swept the dirt anywhere she could hide it, just messed along and slut's wool gathered up all over the house.

Now, the old woman had to go to the store one day. It was a right far piece from where she lived at. So she told that girl she was goin', told her what work she wanted done up 'fore she got back. Then she says to her, says, "And while I'm gone don't ye dare look up the chimney." Then she throwed her bonnet on her head and put out.

So that girl she peeked out the door and watched till the old woman was good and gone, then she ran straight to the fireplace, hunkered down on the hearthrock, and looked up the chimney. Saw a big long leather bag up there on the smokeshelf. Took the poke-stick and gouged it down. Grabbed it up and jerked it open. It was full of big silver dollars and twenty-dollar gold pieces. Well, that girl she took it and broke and run. Out the door she flew. Ran down the road a piece, then she took out across the pasturefield. Came to an old horse standin' out there.

"Good girl! Good girl! Please rub my old sore back. Rub it for me and I'll ride ye."

"I ain't goin' to dirty my pretty white hands. I'm rich! Got no time to fool with ye." And on she went. Came to an old cow.

"Good girl! Good girl! Please milk my old sore bag. Milk me and strip me, and you can have some milk."

"Ain't goin' to dirty my pretty hands. Got no time to fool with such as you. I'm rich now." She went right on. Came to a peach tree.

"Good girl! Good girl! Please pull off these sprouts so they won't choke me so bad. Just prune me a little and you can eat some of my peaches."

"Ain't goin' to do it! But I'm goin' to eat me some peaches anyhow." And she cloomb up in the peach tree, commenced eatin' off all the good ripe peaches. Eat so many she got sleepy and went on off to sleep sittin' up there in the forks of that tree.

Well, the old woman she got back late that evenin', went in the house and hollered for that girl; and when nobody answered she jumped over there and looked up the chimney, and saw her moneybag was gone. She threwed up her hands and run 'round just a-squawlin'. Took out the door and run around the house till she saw which-a-way that girl's tracks went, and down the road she put — a-hollerin' every breath:

> "Gallymanders! Gallymanders!
>   All my gold and silver's gone!
>   My great long moneypurse!"

Came to the horse —

> "Seen a little gal go by here,
>   with a jig and a jag
>   and a long leather bag
>   and all my gold and silver?"

•

"Yes, ma'am!" says the old horse. "Come on! I'll show ye which-a-way she went." So the horse and the old woman went gallopin' off across that pasturefield, the old woman's skirts jest a-floppin'. Came to the fence and the old woman scooted under it and on she went.

"Gallymanders! Gallymanders!
   All my gold and silver's gone!
   My great long moneypurse!"

Came to the cow —

"Seen a little gal go by here,
   with a jig and a jag
   and a long leather bag
   and *all* my gold and silver?"

"Yes, ma'am!" says the cow. "She went right yonder way. You'll soon catch her." On she run.

"Gallymanders! Gallymanders!
   All my gold and silver's gone!
   My great long moneypurse!"

Came to the peach tree —

"Seen a little gal go by here,
   with a jig and a jag
   and a long leather bag
   and *all* my gold and silver?"

"Yes, *ma'am*!" says the peach tree. "She's up here right now. You want her?"

"Yes, I want her," says the old woman.

So the peach tree bent over and dropped that girl out — bumped her right flat on the ground. And the old woman grabbed her and snatched back that moneypurse, and then she took hold on the girl and shook her around considerable, pulled a switch and switched her legs till she run her off from there. Went on home and hid her moneybag back up the chimney.

Well, the old woman she stayed by herself a right long time but she couldn't get her work done up, so she fin'lly sent over the ocean again and hired her another girl. Now this girl was all right: good hand to work. Holp the old woman right well. She never let a shred of slut's wool gather up anywhere in the house. But the old woman treated her awful mean. Wouldn't let her have a thing to eat hardly, kept pilin' more 'n more work on her; but the girl she done the best she could, never said nothin', just worked right on.

So it wasn't long till the old lady she had to go out to the store again. Called that girl, told her what'n-all to do 'fore she got back, says, "And while I'm gone don't ye dare look up the chimney. Ye hear?" And off she went.

Well, that girl she went on about her work: milked the cow and fed the pig and the chickens, washed the dishes and scoured the pots, swept all the floors and made up the beds, scrubbed the kitchen floor, dusted, straightened up everything, swept the yard, churned, hoed the garden, split firewood and carried it in — and then she was done. She she got out her knittin' and sat down in front of the fireplace. She tried awful hard not to think about looking up the chimney but she just couldn't keep it off her mind. She stopped her knittin' after a while, bent over — then she pushed back in her chair and commenced knittin' and rockin' again —

"Ain't a-goin' do it! I ain't goin' do it!"

Then she got tired of knittin', let her knittin' rest in her lap and stopped rockin'. "Now what in this world do you reckon she's got hid up that chimney? — No, I ain't goin' to look. Ain't goin' do it! Ain't goin' do it!" Took up her knittin' and rocked some more.

Well, directly she couldn't stand it no longer. "No harm in just lookin'," she says. So she stooped down and looked right square up the chimney.

"Well, what in the world is that old thing?" she says. Took the poke-stick and gouged it down. Opened it up and then she dumped all that gold and silver out in the floor.

"My! Ain't that pretty!" she says. And she got down on the floor and played with all them silver dollars and twenty-dollar gold pieces a while — piled 'em up, made little pens and fences, till fin'lly she got tired of playin'. So she put all the money back in the moneybag and tried to put it back up the chimney, but it wouldn't go. She tried and she tried, but ever' time it 'uld fall back down. Got the shovel in one hand and the poker in the other — push it up again, and down it come. So she gave up and just left it layin' there in the ashes. Then she got to studyin' about the old woman findin' it out on her, and she got so scared she left there a-runnin'.

Got down the road a piece, decided she'd take out across the field so's not to take any chances on meetin' up with that old woman. Came to the horse.

"Good girl! Good girl! Please rub my old sore back. They rode me so hard yesterday, made my old back awful sore. You rub it for me, and I'll ride ye."

"Well, I'm in a hurry, but I reckon I can do that."

So she pulled her a big handful of grass and rubbed the old horse good. Then he took her up on his back and rode her plumb to the end of the field. She jumped off and on she went. Came to the cow.

"Good girl! Good girl! Please milk my old sore bag. They never milked me this mornin' and my old bag's a-hurtin' me so bad. Milk me and you can have some to drink."

"Well, I'm sort of in a hurry, but I reckon I can do that much for ye."

So she milked the old cow in a little shiny tin bucket was there by the fence. Stripped her good and dry. Had her a drink of milk, and on she went. Came to the peach tree.

"Good girl! Good girl! Please pull off these sprouts. They're chokin' me so bad. You prune me a little and you can have some of my peaches."

"Well, now, I really oughtn't to stop but I reckon I can do it for ye."

So she broke off all the sprouts. Then the peach tree says to her, says, "Now, you climb on up here and get all the ripe peaches you want; and if that old woman comes by here, don't you worry none. I'll handle her."

That girl she hadn't had nothin' to eat but ashcakes and water for I don't know how long and them peaches looked awful good. So she cloomb on up to where she could sit easy-like in the forks of the tree, pulled her off a ripe peach and commenced eatin'.

Well, the old woman got back, run in the house and hollered for that girl, and when the girl never answered, the old woman run quick and looked up the chimney. Throwed back her hands and commenced slappin' her skirts and hollerin' and runnin' all around inside the house and out, a-lookin' for that girl's tracks. Saw which way she left and put out from there a-squallin':

> "Gallymanders! Gallymanders!
> All my gold and silver's gone!
> My great long moneypurse!"

Traced the girl to where the old horse was at —

> "Seen a little gal go by here,
> with a jig and a jag
> and a long leather bag
> and *all* my gold and silver?"

"Ma'am?" says the old horse, and the old woman she had to say it all over again.

"No'm," says the horse. "Hain't seen a soul for quite a spell."

So on she run — flippity-flop! — and she was commencin' to get out of breath —

> "Gallymanders! Gallymanders!
> All my gold and silver's gone! (a-heh!)
> My great long moneypurse!"

Came to the cow —

> "Seen a little gal go by here,
> with a jig and a jag (heh!)
> and a long leather bag (heh!)
> and *all* my gold and silver?"

"Well, now, ma'am," says the cow, "I been right here all evenin' and I ain't seen hardly nobody go by here at all, ma'am."

So the old woman run right on — and she was a-givin' out every step —

> "Gallymanders! Gallymanders! (heh!)
> All my gold and silver's gone (a-heh!)
> My great long moneypurse! (a-heh-a-heh-a-heh!)"

Came to the peach tree —

> "Seen a little gal (heh!)
> go by here (heh!)
> with a jig and a jag
> and a long leather bag (a-heh-i-heh!)
> and *all* my gold and silver? (a-heh-i-heh-i-heh!)"

"No, ma'am," says the peach tree. "She didn't go by here."

So the old woman went right on a-loopety-loop! — with her skirts a-draggin' and her tongue hangin' out and her a-pantin' ever' breath like an old hound dog —

"Gallymanders! Gallymanders!
(A-heh-i-heh-i-heh!)
All my gold and silver's gone!
(a-heh-i-heh-i-heh!)
My great long moneypurse!
(A–heh–i–heh–i–heh–i–heh!)"

Ran till she give plumb out. Man came along and found her 'side the road where she'd give out at, put her in his dump-truck where he'd been haulin' gravel and took her on back to her house, dumped her out by the gate.

They say she never did try to hire no more girls after that. But I never did hear it told whether she fin'lly looked in the ashes and found her old moneypurse or not. Anyhow, last time I was down there she was still so stingy she wouldn't eat nothin' but ashcakes and water.

Harry-cap and the Three Brothers

ALAN GARNER

(Reading time: 8 minutes)

Alan Garner is one of England's most outstanding writers for young people. It is his background in mythology and folklore and his sensitive ear for language that enable him to tell so strongly the stories in A Bag of Moonshine, *one of which is "Harry-cap and the Three Brothers". The fools, hobgoblins, and boggarts that inhabit these stories from the folklore of England and Wales excite listeners and open them up to the wizardry and trickery of the strange and wonderful creatures created for us by a master storyteller.*

This story concerns the strange little man Harry-cap, who points his three brothers towards their varying fortunes, and as the reader you can twist your tongue around the words and phrases that echo hundreds of years of British folklore.

Jack and his two brothers were chopping down trees once, when the oldest brother said, "Cob this for a game!" he says. "I'm off to find better days." And he set down his axe and left the other two to fend for themselves, while he went to seek his fortune.

He walked and he walked, until he was dead beat, and he sat himself down on a hillside to rest. He was just nodding off to sleep, when a little man, as short as old sticks, came up to him and says, "Here, who are you? What are you doing? Where are you going?"

"I'm resting," he says. "And then I'm going looking for better days."

"Well," says the little man, "if you keep on, straight over these hills, you'll come to a white house. Say to them who are there that Harry-cap sent you; and you'll not be wasting your time."

"I'll do that," he says.

So on he walked, over the hills, and he came to a white house; and them who were there said to him, "What do you want?

Where are you from?"

"Harry-cap told me to come," he says.

"Oh, well then; if Harry-cap has sent you, come in and make yourself at home!"

And they took him in, and gave him his supper, and a good wash, and they wouldn't hear of him going any further that night, but he must stop with them and sleep in a proper bed.

He slept well, too, and next morning, as he was making tracks to be on his way, they gave him a leather purse. "You have this purse," they said, "and you'll find you'll never want for money."

He looked in the purse, and there was one gold sovereign lying in it; and that was all.

"Think on," they said; "there'll always be a piece of money in that purse, enough for what you need, neither more nor less."

Well, he thanked them, and went his way; but, after a bit, he thought there was not much use in going further. "For I've got my fortune here," he says. "I might as good go home."

And he turned round and set off back.

It was coming on dark long before he reached home, and he thought he'd treat himself that night; so he stopped off at an inn, and had him a good feed last thing, before he went to bed; and he paid for it out of the purse.

What he didn't know was that the landlord's daughter who served him his supper, she was by way of being something of a witch, and she knew what sort of a purse that was when she saw it. And that night, while he slept, she crept into his room, took his purse, and left another one, looking just like it, in its place; and the fause monkey even put the price of his breakfast in this other purse, so as he wouldn't think anything was wrong in the morning, and he'd be well on his road before he found different.

Next day, he paid for his breakfast, and by nightfall he was home; and his brothers were still mauling with chopping down trees.

"Come and see what I've got," he says, "and fetch the neighbors."

"Now," he says, when they were all in the house, "you tell me what it is you'd like to have, and I'll give you the money for it."

"I could do with a new hat," says Jack.

"I'd like a new pair of britches," says the other brother.

And the neighbors all said what they wanted to have.

"You shall have it," he says. "The money's in here."

But when he opened the purse it was empty. And the neighbors, they winked and blinked like ducks in thunder, and went away, laughing.

"Well," says the second brother, "I think I'll go looking for better days, too. I reckon I can't do worse than him." And next morning, he set off to seek his fortune.

It went the same for him as it had for the oldest. He was on the tramp all day, and sat down to rest on a hillside, and Harry-cap came and asked him what he was doing, and he told him, and Harry-cap sent him to find the white house.

They took him in, and gave him his tea and a bed for the night, and first thing they sat him down at a little round table, and they said, "What will you have for your breakfast?"

"Oh," he says; "ham and eggs."

As soon as he spoke, a sizzling hot plate of ham and eggs appeared out of nowhere. It was that sort of a table. Anything he wanted to eat, he had only to say, and there it was before him.

So he had his breakfast and thanked them, tucked the table under his arm, and went on to seek his fortune.

Now the table, though it wasn't heavy, it was awkward, and he soon got tired of carrying it. "And besides," he says, "it's as good as a fortune. I'd be best at home, not traipsing round with a table."

He turned round and set off back. And with night coming on he arrived at the same inn where the first brother had stayed.

He told the innkeeper he wasn't hungry; he just wanted a bed, he said; and he carried the table upstairs to his room, locked the door, sat himself down, and says to the table, "Roast beef and potatoes and Yorkshire pudding." And there they were, piping hot, and the gravy, too.

But the innkeeper's daughter, the one who was a witch, she'd seen the table on the way in, and she knew what it was for. And she'd crept up, after, and was looking through the keyhole when he had his supper.

That night, when he was asleep, she swopped the table for another like it; it had the same looks, but none of its tricks. And in the morning, he paid his bill, and left, lummoxing the useless table up hill and down dale, and he got back home with the thing just before tea.

"Come and see what I've got," he says; "and fetch the neighbors." And he took the table into the house and set it down on the floor. Jack and the oldest brother came in, with the neighbors following, and the second brother says, "What would you like for your teas?"

"A bacon butty," says Jack.

"A plate of black seams," says the oldest, "with plenty of pepper and vinegar."

"Then all you do is ask," says the second brother. "The table does the rest."

So they asked, Jack and the oldest did; and the neighbors put in their bids, too; but, of course, nothing happened. And the neighbors, they winked and blinked like ducks in thunder, and went away, laughing.

"Now then," says Jack; "it looks like you've flown high and let in a cow-clap at last. I must go see if I can't do as good."

And Jack set off to seek his fortune.

He sat down on the very same hillside, and along came Harry-cap and sent him to the white house, same as he'd done the others. And them that were there fed him and bedded him and sent him away next morning with a good, stout stick in his hand to help him on his road.

"And if you should meet any trouble," they said, "from vagabonds and such, what you do is to say to the stick, 'Stick! Thump 'em!' and your worries will be over.

So Jack set off; and when it was fetching night, he came to the inn where his brothers had stayed. He had supper, and went to bed, leaving the stick where he could see it, on the windowsill.

He blew the candle out, and lay there on his bed, plundering in his mind what he should do to find himself better days, and he was just about to drop off to sleep, when he saw a hand come in at the window and take hold of the stick. It was the innkeeper's daughter, and she was keen to get that stick.

"Eh up!" says Jack. "Stick! Thump 'em!"

And the stick wriggled like a snig in a bottle and began at the innkeeper's daughter, and it thrashed her in through the window and round the room, and gave her the hiding of her life. And Jack wouldn't tell it to leave off till she said she'd fetch him a table and a purse that were magic, if only he'd stop the stick from giving her such a hiding.

So Jack told the stick to stop, and the innkeeper's daughter went and got the table and the purse and handed them over; and Jack told her what he'd do if he ever saw her and her hanky-panky again. Then, in the morning, he set off home, stick in his hand, purse in his pocket, and table on his shoulder.

When he got home, Jack told his brothers to go and invite the neighbors round for a bite to eat. The neighbors came, and Jack sat them down at the table and fed them all big cream teas, with cakes and all the trimmings. Then he took out the purse and gave each of them a golden guinea.

"There," says Jack. "You've had a portion of what my brothers got; would you like to have some of what I found on my travels, now, for being such good neighbors and all?"

"Oh yes!" they said, winking and blinking like ducks in thunder. "Oh, we would! We'd like that very much!"

"Right you are," says Jack. "Then you shall have it. Stick! Thump 'em!"

The stick set about those neighbors and gave them what for. And then it drove them out of the house, down the road, and over the bridge; that's what it did, out of the house, down the road, and over the bridge, till the bridge bended, and my tale's ended.

The Peculiar Such Thing

VIRGINIA HAMILTON

(Reading time: 4 minutes)

Virginia Hamilton is one of the most distinguished writers of fiction for children today. Her anthology, The People Could Fly, *draws upon her lifelong interest in and study of folklore. Her writing echoes her own American black ancestry as she retells the stories that helped keep a culture alive.*

"The Peculiar Such Thing" is a robust tall tale filled with riddles and laughter. It is considered a fairy tale that can be traced to English ones, but this version has a quality of horror that turns it into a ghost story.

As you read the tale, you can build the terror by reading the refrain "Tailypo, tailypo. Give me back my tailypo," louder each time it occurs.

A long time ago way off in the high piney woods lived a fellow all alone. He lived in a one-room log cabin. There was a big old fireplace, and that is where this fellow cooked his supper to eat it right in front of the fire.

One night, after the fellow had cooked and ate his supper, somethin crept through the cracks of the cabin logs. That somethin was the most peculiar such thing the fellow ever saw. And it had a *great, big, long tail.*

As soon as the fellow saw that somethin with its *great, big, long tail*, he reached for his axe. With a swoopin strike with it, he cut the somethin's tail clean off. The peculiar such thing crept away through the cracks between the logs, and was gone.

This fellow, like he had no sense, he cooked the *great, big, long tail.* Yes, he did. It tasted sweet and he ate it. Goodness! And then he went to bed, and in a little while he went off to sleep.

The fellow hadn't been asleep very long before he woke right up again. He heard somethin climbin up the side of his cabin. It sounded mighty like a cat. He could hear it scratchin and tearin away. And pretty soon he heard it say, *"Tailypo, tailypo.*

Give me back my tailypo."

Now the fellow living there all alone did have some dogs. Big one was Best and the other two slight ones was All Right and Fair. And when that fellow heard somethin, he called his dogs, "Yuh! Dawgs! Come on!" like that. And his dogs come flyin out from under the cabin. And they chased the peculiar such thing away down a far piece. Then this fellow went on back to bed. He went to sleep.

It was deep in the middle of the next night when the fellow woke up. He heard somethin by his front door tryin to get in. He listened hard and he could hear it scratchin and tearin away. And he heard it say, *"Tailypo, tailypo. Give me back my tailypo."*

Fellow sat up in his bed. He called his dogs, "Yuh! You, Best, you All Right, you Fair, come on in!" like that. And the dogs busted around the corner. And they caught up with the peculiar such thing at the gate, and they about broke their own tails tryin to catch it. This time they chased what it was down into the big hollow there. And the fellow, well, he went back to bed and went to sleep.

It was way long toward mornin, the fellow woke up and he hears somethin down in the big swamp. He had to listen. He heard it say, *"You know you got it. I know you know. Give me back my tailypo."*

That man sat up in bed. He called his dogs, "You the Best, you All Right, and you Fair. Yuh! Come on in here!"

Well, this time, the dogs never come. The thing down there in the hollow musta carried them off in there. It musta eaten the first one, says, *"That's best."* It eaten the other two, says, *"That ain't but all right and fair."*

And the fellow went back to bed. Don't see how he could sleep again. But he didn't know how bad off his dogs was by then.

Well, it was just daybreak. The fellow was awake. Scared, he didn't know why. Musta heard somethin. Somethin right there with him in the room. It sounded like a cat climbin up the covers at the foot of his bed. He listened. He could hear it, scratchin and tearin away.

The fellow look at the foot of his bed. He's seein two little pointy ears comin up over the edge of the bed. In another minute, he's seein two big, scary-red eyeballs lookin straight at him. He can't say nothin. He can't scream, he's too scared to death.

That peculiar such thing at the foot of the bed kept on creepin up, creepin up. By and by, it was right on top of the fellow. And it said in his face in a real low voice, *"Tailypo, tailypo. Give me back my tailypo."*

That man loses his voice, loses his power of speech. But finally, he can say it. Says, "I hasn't got it. I hasn't got your tailypo!"

And that somethin that was there, that peculiar such thing, says right back, *"Yes you has!"* It jumped on that fellow and it was fierce. Its big teeth tore at him, made him ribbons. They say it got its tailypo back.

Fellow's cabin fall to ruin. It rot. It crumble and it disappear. Nothin left to it in the big woods but the place where it was.

And the folks that live near that place say that deep in the night, when the moon is goin down and the wind blows across the place just right, you can hear some peculiar such thing callin, *"Tailypo, tailypo . . ."* like that. And then, the sound of it do just fade away with the moonlight. Like it never even ever was.

The Blue Bottle

EDNA O'BRIEN

(Reading time: 9 minutes)

The well-known writer Edna O'Brien called upon her Irish heritage to create her anthology of fairy tales, Tales for the Telling. *While myth and legend shape the stories, a trace of realism gives an immediacy that will draw today's children to them. With her acclaimed mastery of the narrative form and her natural ear for the language of rural and small-town Ireland, Edna O'Brien provides us with richly detailed classic tales of broken promises, curses, and giants.*

"The Blue-Bottle" is a tale of good luck gone bad, and you will hear echoes of all of the "wishes" that various country folk had misused in centuries of storytelling. The Irish dialect may require a rehearsal or two, but the words are crafted in such a way that the story almost tells itself.

There lived a poor man with his wife and several children and they had to exist on the scrapings from their few acres of rocky land. One summer there was torrential rain — the oats they had sown got destroyed, the chickens died of the pip, the pig got pneumonia and the poor man didn't have the money to pay his rent.

"Oh Mary what shall we do?" said he to his wife.

"Wisha, then, mavoureen, what can we do but sell the cow?"

"What will we do when she's gone?" said he.

"We'll have to trust in God," said she.

So the next day he set out for the fair of Cork. His wife shook holy water on himself and the beast and it was a long and a lonesome walk he had, talking to the cow to keep himself company.

He found himself in the middle of a lonely moor and came to a spot where there was a clump of hazel trees. He thought he heard a whistle, something similar to the curlew's cry, and then the cow shied and tried to break away. Before his eyes there sauntered forth a little man about three feet high in a frieze coat that came to the ground. He had a wrinkled face, skin the color of cauliflower, no nose and little scalding eyes.

"Where are you going with the cow?" said he in a piping voice.

"I'm having to sell her," said the farmer, flabbergasted at the sight of the stranger.

"That means you have no money," said the little man. "I could give you this bottle," said he, producing a dark blue bottle from under his coat. It was a humble-looking thing such as you would find tossed in any ditch.

"It's worth thousands of pounds," said the little man.

"Do you think I'm a fool?" said the farmer.

"You won't be sorry if you take it," said the little man.

"It's money I need," said the farmer.

"This bottle is better than any money, Mick Boland."

Mick started and asked the little man how he knew his name.

"I know you and I have a regard for you," said he and then pointing to the cow he said it wouldn't surprise him if she didn't die of hunger and exhaustion before they got to the fair at all.

"You're trying to worry me," said Mick.

"I'm trying to bring you good luck," said the little man.

"Faith, I need luck," said Mick as he thought on how destitute they were.

"Then give me the cow and take the bottle and when you go home do as I say."

Mick was in a quandary because he was half-believing the little man.

"Take it and be rich, refuse it and be a pauper."

Mick stared at him, trying to decide; then all of a sudden he seized the bottle and said, "If you're lying to me the curse of the poor will be on you."

"I have spoken the truth and now you must do what I tell you."

"What's that?" said Mick.

"When you go home, never mind if your wife is angry, get her to sweep the floor, set a cloth on the table and put the bottle on the ground saying these words, 'Bottle do your duty.' "

"Is that all?" said Mick.

"That's it," said the stranger, "off with you now, and rejoice — you're a rich man."

"God grant it," said Mick as he saw his cow being driven

away. He began to retrace his steps but when he looked back neither the cow nor the man was to be seen.

He went on home muttering prayers and holding on to his bottle. At one point he slipped and thought it had broken, so after that he put it inside his shirt, next to his skin. He kept thinking about the trouble he'd be in with his wife and at the same time speculating on the powers of the bottle.

"Oh Mick, you're back," said his wife, surprised that he'd been there and back so soon. She asked who bought the cow and how much money he got.

"I don't know who bought her," said Mick wondering how he'd tell his tale and dreading her temper.

"But where's the money?" said she.

"Be quiet now," said he and took out the bottle and laid it on the table. "That's what I got for the cow."

"Oh you fool, and you bostoon," said she and asked in the name of God how they would pay their rent and what they would eat for their supper.

"Be patient," said he and he told her about the strange little man and the promises he'd made.

"Blood and Blunderbusses," said she and she seized the bottle and would have broken it but that he grasped it from her and held it tight. Then he told her the story from start to finish. Whether it was the way he told it or whether it was that the poor desperate woman would try any remedy, she got up quietly, she began to sweep the floor, she tidied around, she pulled out the table, she spread the cloth on it and then waited anxiously. Mick put the bottle on the ground, pointed his finger at it and said, "Bottle do your duty."

"Look, look," said one of their little children, as two tiny little sprites rose up out of the bottle and in an instant covered the table with gold plates and dishes, then filled the plates with the most delicious roast and victuals and put jugs of ale down. Having done that they slid back down into the bottle again and Mick and his family sat down at the table to eat.

"'Tis a long road that has no turning," said Mick, prouder than he had ever been.

"I wonder if they'll take these gold dishes away," said Mary and they waited but no one came.

A few days later Mick sold the gold plates and with the money bought a horse and cart, and warm clothes for his children. No matter what they wanted, Mick had only to say "Bottle do your duty" and it was granted. The word got around that they were beginning to show signs of great prosperity so the landlord drove over one day and asked Mick where he suddenly got his money.

"It's not from a few barren acres of land," said the landlord.

Mick couldn't help boasting about the bottle and of course as he did the landlord coveted it. He offered Mick a great deal of money but Mick did not need money. Then he offered him a big farm with stables and cattle on the land and Mick was not able to refuse it. He would be a gentleman at last. He handed over the bottle and very soon was installed in his new farm. He lived lavishly, invented a coat of arms for himself, sent to France for wine, to Russia for caviar and to Italy for marble mantelpieces and furniture. As time went on his money ran out, his friends began to desert him and soon he was a pauper.

Mick and his wife decided that he should do as before, that he should set out for the fair with his only cow, that he should take the exact same route and that most likely he'd meet his little man.

It was very misty the morning he set out. He and the cow crossed the valley and then took the main road until they reached the track that led to the moor. He came to the hazel clump and sure enough the cow shied and he heard the voice of the little man.

"I told you you'd be rich," said the little man.

"I'm not rich now," said Mick. "I want another bottle and I'll give you this cow."

"Here you are," said the little man. "And you know what to do with it."

Mick ran as fast he could, eager to set his bottle down at home and bedeck himself with fine things and loot. Seeing him come in such excitement, his wife ran out to meet him.

Once at home his wife did as before. She swept the floor, put the cloth on the table and waited for Mick to give the order.

"Bottle do your duty."

Well as soon as he said it, two strong hobos with big cudgels came out of the bottle and struck Mick a blow, then his wife, then all the bairns, till they lay in a heap on the floor yellling and roaring. Soon as he came to his senses Mick got up and was relieved to find that the hobos had gone back into the bottle and all was quiet except for his children mewling. He picked up the bottle, put it inside his vest and set off for the landlord's house. A servant met him at the door and wasn't at all inclined to let him in.

"Tell your master I have another bottle," said Mick.

"Capital . . . capital," said the servant and he led him into the great hall.

The landlord was having his breakfast and when Mick told him the news the landlord asked if it was as good as the first.

"It's better," said Mick.

He could see his own bottle up on the mantelshelf and was thinking to himself that it would shortly be in his possession.

"Show us," said the landlord.

Mick set the second bottle on the table and gave the instructions. Out stepped the two villains and in no time the landlord and his family were sprawled on the floor with crockery and fried eggs and porridge heaped over them.

"Stop these devils, Mick Boland, or I'll have you hanged," said the landlord from under the table.

"I won't stop them till I get my own bottle back," said Mick.

"Take it and clear out," said the landlord.

Mick jumped on a chair, picked up his own bottle, put it inside his shirt and ordered the two villains to create a bit more rumpus in order to give him a chance to escape.

As he was crossing the moor he met with the little man.

"Let me see the bottle to make sure it came to no harm."

As soon as Mick handed it over he saw the little man grinning and cuddling it to his chest and he knew that he was not going to get it back.

"Give me one last chance," he begged.

"You've had your chance."

"I was a fool," said Mick.

"Aye," laughed the little man and without further ado he disappeared and in his place there stood a bit of a broken tree with a crow cawing on it and staring at Mick with blood-red eyes. Mick called and called but only the crow answered. They named the spot "Bealnabuideal" (the mouth of the bottle) and there are people that still believe that on some lonesome journey, some poor farmer will meet the little man who will give him the bottle in exchange for a cow.

The Snake-Bit Hoe Handle

DOC McCONNELL

(Reading time: 4 minutes)

Over the years, I have read this tale in different versions in dozens of books, in the original Sounds of Language Readers *by Bill Martin, Jr., and in various American folklore anthologies. It is a perfect example of the tall tale genre, building upon a simple incident a network of exaggerations.*

In this story, the ending adds an interesting twist to the proceedings and the reader must carefully follow each episode so that the outcome will make sense. It is a story that calls for an expressive and relaxed reading, for much of the joy in telling tall tales comes from the fun of the audience being in on the joke all along.

When I was growin' up, it seemed like all I ever done was hoe corn. I'd hoe corn from mornin' to night. One day, I was out in the field a-hoein' corn and, as I was lookin' outa the corner of one eye, there in that corn patch was a great big ol' copperheaded rattlesnake. You'd never seen such a snake in your life. He rared back at me, and I rared back at him with my hoe. I took a swing at that ol' snake, missed 'im, and hit a rock and broke the hoe outa the end of my hoe handle. That ol' rattlesnake sunk them teeth into the grain of that hoe handle and held on for dear life. Down through the cornfield we went. I would shake him awhile, and he would shake me awhile. We got clear down to the end of the corn patch before I finally shook that ol' snake offa the end of my hoe handle.

I ran to the house, throwed that ol' hoe handle down at the garden fence, and said, "Pa, you won't believe what's happened to me out there in the cornfield. I jist seen the biggest snake up there on that ridge as you've ever seen. He bit my hoe handle, and I hit a rock and broke my hoe offa the end of my hoe handle, and I ain't a-goin' back into that cornfield no more."

Pa said, "Son, I know what you're a-tryin' to do. You're jist tryin' to git outa hoein' corn. You jist go out there and git that

49

hoe handle and bring it to me and I'll put you a new hoe on the end of that handle."

Well, I went out to the garden fence and started to pick up that hoe handle, and you ain't a-goin' to believe this. Where that snake's poison had soaked into the grain of the wood of that ol' hoe handle, it had done started swellin' up. It commenced to swellin' and swellin' and swellin' from the poison until that hoe handle was as big 'round as a baseball bat — and ten feet long. I couldn't believe it.

So, I took that ol' hoe handle to show Pa and he said, "Why, we'll jist have to make some kindlin' wood outa that hoe handle. Run out and git the axe."

By the time I got back, the hoe handle had kept a-swellin' and a-swellin' and a-swellin' so that it was as big 'round as a water bucket.

Pa said, "We'll just have to saw that ol' hoe handle up for firewood. Git the crosscut saw."

So I went over to the woodshed to git the saw, and by the time I got back, that hoe handle was as big as a wagon wheel — and over seventy-two feet long.

"Why," Pa said, "there ain't nothin' to do now but to take that hoe handle down there to the sawmill and have it sawed up for lumber."

It was so big now that we could barely git it in our wagon. And as that ol' team of mules pulled that log to the mill, that hoe handle drug a big trench right down the middle of the road.

Well, they sawed all day Friday and 'till dinner on Saturday. And when they was done, they had sawed 746,362 board feet of lumber from that ol' hoe handle. It jist kept on a-swellin' and a-swellin', and by the time we got that lumber stacked up, we had twenty-two wagonloads of lumber. We hauled that lumber home, and Pa sat out there and looked at that pile of lumber and thought and thought.

Finally on Monday mornin', he said, "You boys git outa bed. We're a-goin' to build a chicken house."

Well, we commenced to sawin' and hammerin' them boards, and when we was done, we had one of the finest chicken houses in Tucker's Knob. It was a purtty structure — twenty-two foot long, seventeen foot deep, and nine foot high in the front. We had boxes for layin', and little poles for roostin'. It was a nice-lookin' building.

And as we were standin' back admirin' our new chicken house that afternoon, Pa said, "Son, that chicken house needs one thing before we've completed our job. We need to put a good coat of paint on our new chicken house. Run and git us some paint."

So I went down to John Mauk's store and bought five gallons of the purttiest striped paint that you've ever seen. We commenced to paintin' that chicken house, and we painted way up into the evenin' 'til it was jist gittin' dusky dark. And when we finished, we stood back to admire our work, and all of a sudden, we heard this creakin' and moanin' and groanin' and that chicken house commenced to shakin' and movin' 'round.

You see, I had mixed some turpentine in that paint, and that turpentine that I'd used to thin the paint was such good medicine that it started takin' the swellin' outa that lumber. And that chicken house went to shrinkin' and shrinkin' and shrinkin'. And when it got done shrinkin', it wasn't no bigger than a shoe box. And it's a good thing we hadn't put our chickens in it, 'cause they'd ever' one been killed, I know.

The New Legend of Sam Peppard

CELIA LOTTRIDGE

(Reading time: 14 minutes)

Celia Lottridge is an accomplished Canadian writer and storyteller. Her background in children's literature provides her with an in-depth understanding of what children respond to in a story.

In her preface to "The New Legend of Sam Peppard", in Tales for an Unknown City, *edited by Dan Yashinky, Celia Lottridge informs us that what happens in her story did actually happen, and that she went to school with some of Sam's great-grandchildren. However, legends are born from what we don't know, from what disappears from one telling to another, and in her story, Celia tells us what now belongs to her and us — the new legend of Sam Peppard.*

The wind blew Sam Peppard to Oskaloosa. It was blowing strong out of the west, and if there had been any old-timers they might have squinted up at the dark clouds blown to rags as the wind pushed them east and shaken their heads. But everyone in Oskaloosa had arrived from back east not more than eighteen months before. They were building a town in the rolling hills at the edge of the real west and wind or no wind it was not surprising to see a young man with a bag full of tools swing down from one of the big wagons that hauled folks too poor to have a wagon of their own. Sam stood in the wide, dusty street that was destined to be the north side of the square and said, "I just blew in from the west. Does this town need a blacksmith?"

Oskaloosa needed wagon-wheel rims and nails and hinges. There were always horses and mules to be shod, and besides that, like every town it needed a blacksmith shop so that folks would have a place to hang around. When they found out that Sam had been nearly everywhere and would tell about it, Sam's shop was always hopping.

"I like this place," said Sam. "It's right on the edge of the east and the west and the north and the south. Some day it will be dead centre of this country."

Sam lived in a room behind his shop, and every morning he would step out the front door of his shop and feel the wind. If it blew from the north, south, or west he would step right back in and start to work. But if the wind was from the east he would stand there in the middle of the street with his back to the wind and stretch his arms out until the wind whipped his shirt-tails around his ears. Folks got used to it but they teased him some: "That wind is gonna blow you straight to Denver some day." "Next time I go west that's the way I'm going," Sam would say. "No more ox-carts for me."

The country around Oskaloosa was a jumping-off place for people travelling west. Just north ran the Oregon Trail and just south ran the Santa Fe Trail. So folks had a choice of route. But, it was true, they all went by ox-cart. Prairie schooners they were called; but they lumbered over the flat prairie at a mighty slow rate.

Sam thought about all those miles of waving prairie grass. "If those were waves of water, those prairie schooners would be a pretty sight sailing before the wind," he said to his friend Joe.

One winter day, the folks who made a habit of warming themselves beside Sam's smithy fire found him building something. It looked suspiciously like a wagon box. Funny shape though. "Eight feet long, three feet wide," Sam said when they asked him, and he wouldn't explain why.

He wouldn't explain why the wheels were so high either, or why the metal rims were so thick. When they asked him why he was fiddling around with some contraption at the back off the wagon and how in tarnation he was going to hitch any horse or ox to the front, Sam just said, "This isn't a horse-cart or an ox-cart either."

One morning Joe went into Sam's shop and he found Sam fixing something that looked exactly like a mast in the front of the wagon. "What is this thing you're building?" he said. "Are you aiming to put a sail to a wagon?"

"Joe," said Sam, "I'm aiming to use the wind. There's more wind than anything else out there on the prairie, and a lot of the time it's blowing towards the west. Why can't it take folks along with it? Some of them will want to be coming back, too.

They can take the wind that blows towards the east. Think of it, Joe. Sails across the prairie."

Joe shook his head, but he caught a little of what Sam was seeing. "You gonna call it a sailing wagon?"

"A wind wagon. That's what it is. A wind wagon," said Sam Peppard.

News of what Sam was building in his shop was all over town by ten a.m. and by noon, nearly everyone who could walk had come by to look at it. Most had quite a bit to say to Sam, generally along the lines of "Sam, you're crazier than we thought you were."

Some got around to asking, "Where you planning to go in that thing?"

"Denver," said Sam. "I've heard they've made silver strikes in the mountains up behind Denver. I figured the wind wagon would be the best way to get there."

"Denver's six hundred miles!"

"There's wind all the way," said Sam.

After that, Sam got hardly a minute's peace; and, sociable as he was, he got pretty tired of admitting that he might be crazy but nevertheless, he was headed for Denver.

Some good did come of it, though. Joe decided to go with Sam. "I've taken a pretty good look at that wagon of yours," he said. "I don't see how you can manage that sail and that steering stick at the same time. I'll come along and give you a hand."

"That's a tiller," said Sam. "You're going to be glad you came."

Also, Mary Alice Bellows said she would make the sail. "Blacksmith you may be, Sam Peppard, and carpenter too; but I don't think sewing is in a man's line at all."

Sam didn't tell her about the master sail-makers he had seen back in Maine. He knew sewing wasn't his line. "I'll bring you a silver locket," He said. "I thank you kindly, Miz Bellows."

The only real aggravation Sam had was an old man who had come in from a claim to the south and west of Oskaloosa. He appeared in the door of Sam's shop one day towards closing time and leaned against the door post like a narrow gray shadow. "Thought you ought to know my shack blew away."

"Too bad," said Sam.

"Cow too."

Sam said nothing.

"Wind's mighty strong out there."

There was a long pause. "My wind wagon, she's made to go with the wind."

There was a longer pause. "There's go with," said the old man, "and then there's blown away. Can't see there's much difference."

After that he'd come and stand in the doorway every day or two and just stare at the wind wagon and shake his head.

Sam ignored him as best he could. The wind wagon was almost ready to go, and he had to work ahead to cover some of the two months he figured he'd be gone.

As he worked, he stopped now and then to add a little touch to the wind wagon. He painted her name — *Wind Wagon, Oskaloosa* — on her back panel. He polished up the brass fitting of the mast. He greased the big iron wheels until they turned sweetly, without a murmur of complaint.

One day Joe dropped by. "I've been thinking, Sam," he said. "The two of us aren't going to be enough. Think about it, Sam. Managing the sail, steering the thing, keeping a lookout for trouble, gathering buffalo chips so as we can have a fire, cooking, shooting rabbits to eat. We'll be too tired to go looking for gold and silver when we get there."

"Who did you have in mind?" said Sam.

"Well, there's the Graham boys. They don't talk much and I reckon they're a pretty good shot. One of them plays the banjo too."

Sam knew the Graham boys all right. They were the two most up and coming of a large, shiftless family that lived on the edge of town. Their names were Abraham and Isaiah, but no one ever remembered which was which; and they were both tall and lanky and silent, so they were just called the Graham boys.

"I don't guess they'd have got themselves steady jobs," said Sam. "I'll talk to them about it."

When he did, the boys looked at each other and allowed as how they weren't too busy this time of the year and they wouldn't mind setting eyes on the Rocky Mountains. But they did have one question. "How's that fool wagon of yours going to get us there?"

"She'll get us there," said Sam. "I'm just waiting for the right kind of wind."

It was a wind towards the west he needed, and all the wind that spring seemed to come from the west. Sam shook his head every morning when he came in from testing the wind. "There's one thing the wind wagon can't do, Joe," he said one day. "She can't sail into the wind. If it's coming from the northeast, now, or the southeast, we can just angle the sail a little and she'll go easy. But straight from the west, there's not much we can do."

One Saturday, when Sam went out into the street in front of the shop, the wind was from the west all right, but it was so fresh and so sweet that Sam locked up the shop and went to look for Joe and the Graham boys.

"We've got to try her out today," he told them. "I swear I can smell the snow melting in the high mountains and the flowers blooming in the foothills. One of these days the wind will be just right and we've got to be ready to go."

So they hauled the wind wagon, by hand, to a big high piece of ground just south of town. It was about as flat as any place around Oskaloosa, but it had a steep slope at the east end.

"Perfect," said Sam. "Folks think the prairies is flat as a pancake but we might have to handle a few hills."

It was a tight squeeze in the wind wagon when they were all on board, and one of the Graham boys said, "Don't know where you expect me to stick a banjo." But then Joe hoisted the sail and they were off. Sam felt the wind in his hair. There was nothing ahead of the wagon. No horse, no ox. Just the grassy field. It pulled itself under the wagon wheels smooth as silk. Well, not exactly. The wagon lurched and bumped along and the Graham boys hung on for their lives. Their faces were as white as if a raging sea awaited them if they fell overboard, instead of Old Man Hicks's pasture.

All Sam could feel was the wind pushing them. It was solid, it was strong. It could push them all the way to Denver.

Some movement against the trees caught his eye. He turned away from the onrushing pasture and saw the old man from the claim. He was watching the wind wagon with fierce eyes and Sam wondered for a second whether he wanted them to blow away or whether he hoped they wouldn't. Just then, the land sloped sharply down. The wind was under the flaring sides of the wagon body. It was ballooning the sail and lifting the wind wagon off the ground. It occurred to Sam that the wind might blow them all the way to the Missouri River. Then they were beyond the crest of the hill. The wind slackened, the wheels touched the earth again and bumped to a stop. After a minute they all got out and looked at the wind wagon. She was fine. No cracks, no bends.

"Well," said Sam, "she takes to the wind. Give her a high enough hill and she might just take off. We'll put a little ballast in front to keep her bow down. We won't take to the air again. I guarantee."

The next day Sam was painting over a few scratches on the wagon box when he looked up to see the old-timer from the claim standing in the doorway. "You'd better get that thing fixed so it stays on the ground," he said. "The wind's about to change."

Sam couldn't think of anything to say for a minute, which was unusual for him. But he collected himself. "We're ready," he said. "She'll make it to Denver. And back. I'll bring you some gold nuggets."

But the old-timer shook his head. "Just keep that wagon on the ground," he said. "The wind out there . . ." He shook his head again. And then he was gone.

The wind changed the next day. It blew out of the east straight and true, as if it intended to blow that direction till Christmas. But Sam knew better. He collected Joe and the Graham boys. They packed up the sourdough and beans they had ready, found a tight corner for the banjo and a deck of cards and sent out the word that the wind wagon was ready to go.

Everyone in Oskaloosa showed up for the great send-off, except for a few sceptics who claimed they would all be home by sundown. Sam couldn't help looking for the old-timer but his lean figure and grim countenance were nowhere to be seen.

Sam stood up in the back of the wind wagon, waved his broad-rimmed hat to the crowd, and said, "Folks, if you want to beat us to Denver you should have started off three weeks ago." Then he sat down, set the hat squarely on his head to shade his eyes from the brilliant sun, and took hold of the tiller. Joe pulled the sail around till the wind caught it, several boys ran alongside to give a push, and the wind wagon, creaking a little, sailed off along the ridge road leading west out of town.

Two long days later they reached the edge of the Flint Hills where the land quits rolling and levels out into a five-hundred-mile slow upward incline to the foot of the Rocky Mountains. Before them lay the hard-packed road to Denver, rutted and worn down by the wheels of all the wagons carrying people who had headed west looking for land or gold or silver. In fact, in the distance they could see quite a swarm of prairie schooners lurching along.

"Come on, boys," said Sam Peppard, "we'll catch 'em before the sun is high!" He stretched his arms out as wide as he could and felt that strong wind from the east pulling at his shirt sleeves. This time he knew he was going with it.

For the first week or so the wind was strong and steady. The wind wagon rolled along overtaking other kinds of wagons regularly. Drivers and passengers risked falling off their seats as they stared at the oxless wind wagon careening past them.

Then there were several days of calm, and the folks in some of the slow, steady, ox-drawn wagons had the satisfaction of seeing the wind wagon drawn off the trail while its crew played cards and went rabbit hunting. They did not keep their pleasure to themselves. "Never mind," said Sam. "They'll be looking at our dust soon enough."

And Sam was right. When the wind started up again it was fresher and stronger than ever. They soon passed the main body of wagons and for days the wind wagon rolled along so fast and smooth that even the Graham boys had to admit that it looked like they would live to see the Rocky Mountains.

On one of those days Sam said, "I'd wager we're going twenty-five miles an hour." Since none of the others had any notion except that they were going mighty fast, they didn't argue with Sam; but one of the Graham boys, who happened to have the rear lookout spot, said, "Well, I sure hope those Indians can't ride twenty-five miles an hour."

They all looked where he was looking and, sure enough, there were three Indians on spotted horses riding hell for leather in their direction. Now Sam hoped he had never done anything to make any Indians sore at him, but he knew that a lot of Indians had a lot to be sore about; so he wasn't sure those Indians had friendly thoughts in their minds. And they were certainly coming on fast.

"Come on, Wind Wagon," he said, "now's the time to show what you can do." They all hunkered down to give the sail a chance to do the most it could and Sam fiddled with the tiller.

Joe lifted his head above the edge of the boards and said, "By gum, Sam, I think they're racing us."

Then, they all looked at the Indians and saw that they were riding alongside the wind wagon, about a hundred yards to the south. Sam grinned. "Well, they've got themselves a race," he said.

The wind was with them that day, and after maybe ten miles of hard riding the Indians were still behind the wagon. They waved their hands over their heads in a friendly fashion and rode off to the south. That night Sam went to sleep knowing that the wind wagon could surely go with the wind.

And the wind kept getting stronger and stronger as the land rose towards the Rockies. Some days they didn't put the sail all the way up. "Either it will get blown to rags, or that wind will take us right up into the air," said Sam. "It's just too bad that being blown away can't get you where you're going."

After three weeks Sam said, "I reckon we're just about eighty miles from Denver." They were feeling good. The Rocky Mountains were a solid cloud on the horizon, and the Graham boys were beginning to fret about how they were ever going to climb so high. Sam was feeling a bit agitated, but he figured that it was because he hated to come to the end of the wind wagon's first voyage. He did notice that there were some dark clouds to the southwest, but there was blue sky overhead and the wind had calmed down some.

Sam was just shaking his head a little, wondering whether folks back in Oskaloosa would believe they had done it, when suddenly an immense gust of wind hit the wind wagon broadside and at the same time Joe hollered, "It's a twister!"

Sam looked. Coming out of the southwest was a thin, black finger of wind, twisting and snaking its way straight at the wind wagon, roaring like a thousand mad bulls. Sam gripped the tiller. It seemed as if he should be able to dodge something so narrow. But the next split second he knew that if that twister wanted the wind wagon, there was nothing he could do about it.

"Jump, boys!" he yelled. But there wasn't time. That twister picked up the wind wagon with Sam hanging onto the tiller and everybody else hanging onto anything they could grab. Sam felt the huge force of that wind as it lifted him and the wagon and Joe and the Graham boys and held them all twenty feet above the prairies for so long that he could have drawn a deep breath, if he had been breathing. Then it dropped them, wind wagon and all, in a heap on the ground.

Sam looked around at his crew. They were all in one piece, shaking their heads and cautiously moving their arms and legs. But the wind wagon was in a thousand pieces. Sam looked at the tangle of sail and the splintered boards and bent wheels. "Well, boys," he said, "it looks like we walk the rest of the way. But she sure gave us some ride, didn't she?"

As it turned out, one of the lumbering freight wagons came along and, with a few smirks and rude jokes, the driver offered them a ride into Denver. "Unless my team gets blowed away, of course."

Sam found the back panel with the proud words *Wind Wagon, Oskaloosa* painted on it. It was hardly scratched. Sam put it under his arm, climbed aboard the freight wagon, and rode into Denver.

That's almost the end of the story. Sam, Joe, and the Graham boys did go silver mining before they hopped another wagon back to Oskaloosa, and Sam brought home enough silver to build himself a nice little house.

"This is where I'm going to stay," he said. And he did. He married, had ten children, and lived to be known for his long white beard.

And as for the old-timer? He showed up the day Sam stoked up the fire in his shop. "You gonna build another one of them wagons?" he asked. "Or have you had enough?"

"If I build another wind wagon," said Sam, "I'd never find a wind like I found the first time. I reckon I've gotten the most out of a wind wagon that I ever could."

So Oskaloosa never did get famous for wind wagons. But it's still there, nearly dead centre of the country, just like Sam Peppard said it would be.

The Origin of Death

JOSEPH BRUCHAC

(Reading time: 3 minutes)

Joseph Bruchac is an award-winning poet, novelist, and storyteller who follows the traditional ways of his Amerindian heritage. The stories from Keepers of the Earth *are "lesson" stories from the native oral tradition, and centre upon the relationships of people to nature. As well, these tales celebrate and affirm the human spirit.*

"The Origin of Death" is a story from the Blackfeet (Siksika), who lived in Northern Montana and Southern Alberta. They were hunters of the buffalo and lived in cone-shaped lodges covered with buffalo skin. This very short story is a creation tale, and can lead to much discussion about the fairness of the choices life forces on us.

When the world was new, Old Man and Old Woman were walking around.

"Let us decide how things will be," Old Man said.

"That is good," said Old Woman. "How shall we do it?"

"Well," Old Man said, "since it was my idea I think I should have the first say in everything."

"That is good," said Old Woman, "just as long as I have the last say."

So they walked around and looked at things. Then Old Man spoke. "I have been thinking about hunting," he said. "The men will be the hunters. Anytime they want to shoot an animal they will call it and it will come to them."

"I agree men should be the hunters," Old Woman said. "But if the animals come when they are called, life will be too easy for the people. The animals should run away when they see the people. Then it will be hard for the men to kill them. That way people will be smarter and stronger."

"You have the last say," Old Man agreed. Then they walked around some more.

After a while, Old Man spoke again. "I have been thinking

about what people will look like," he said. "They will have eyes on one side of their face and their mouth on the other. Their mouths will go straight up and down. They will have ten fingers on each hand."

"I agree that people should have their eyes and their mouth on their faces," Old Woman said. "But their eyes will be at the top of their face and their mouth at the bottom and they will be set across. I agree they should have fingers on their hands, but ten on each hand will make them clumsy. They will have five fingers on each hand."

"You have the lat say," Old Man agreed.

Now they were walking by the river. "Let us decide about life and death," Old Man said. "I will do it this way. I will throw this buffalo chip into the river. If it floats, when people die they will come back to life after four days and then live forever."

Old Man threw the buffalo chip into the water. It bobbed up and floated. "I agree we should decide it this way," Old Woman said. "But I do not think it should be done with a buffalo chip. I will throw this stone into the water instead. If it floats, the people will die for four days and then come back to life and live forever. If it sinks, the people will not come back to life after they die."

Old Woman threw the stone into the water. It sank immediately.

"That is the way it should be," Old Woman said. "If people lived forever, the Earth would be too crowded. There would not be enough food. This way people will feel sorry for each other. There will be sympathy in the world."

Old Man said nothing.

Some time passed. Old Woman had a child. She and Old Man loved the child very much and they were happy. One day, though, the child became sick and died. Then Old Woman went to Old Man.

"Let us have our say again about death," she said.

But Old Man shook his head. "No," he said, "you had the last say."

Spirits of the Railway

PAUL YEE

(Reading time: 7 minutes)

Paul Yee, a noted historian and children's author, has based the stories in his collection Tales from Gold Mountain *on the experiences of Chinese immigrants who came to Canada to work on the building of the Canadian Pacific Railway. He has woven into this history the rich folktale traditions brought from China to create powerful stories that work on many different levels.*

In "Spirits of the Railway", a young man attempts to appease the ghosts of dead Chinese railway workers by honoring the request of his father. The tale is full of ghosts, danger, and tension, and all age groups will relish its impact.

One summer many, many years ago, heavy floodwaters suddenly swept through south China again. Farmer Chu and his family fled to high ground and wept as the rising river drowned their rice crops, their chickens, and their water buffalo.

With their food and farm gone, Farmer Chu went to town to look for work. But a thousand other starving peasants were already there. So when he heard there was work across the ocean in the New World, he borrowed some money, bought a ticket, and off he sailed.

Long months passed as his family waited to hear from him. Farmer Chu's wife fell ill from worry and weariness. From her hard board bed she called out her husband's name over and over, until at last her eldest son borrowed money to cross the Pacific in search of his father.

For two months, young Chu listened to waves batter the groaning planks of the ship as it crossed the ocean. For two months he dreaded that he might drown at any minute. For two months he thought of nothing but his father and his family.

Finally he arrived in a busy port city. He asked everywhere for his father, but no one in Chinatown had heard the name. There were thousands of Chinese flung throughout the New

65

World, he was told. Gold miners scrabbled along icy rivers, farmers ploughed the long low valleys, and laborers traveled through towns and forests, from job to job. Who could find one single man in this enormous wilderness?

Young Chu was soon penniless. But he was young and strong, and he feared neither danger nor hard labor. He joined a work gang of thirty Chinese, and a steamer ferried them up a river canyon to build the railway.

When the morning mist lifted, Chu's mouth fell open. On both sides of the rushing river, gray mountains rose like walls to block the sky. The rock face dropped into ragged cliffs that only eagles could ascend and jutted out from cracks where scrawny trees clung. Never before had he seen such towering ranges of dark raw rock.

The crew pitched their tents and began to work. They hacked at hills with hand-scoops and shovels to level a pathway for the train. Their hammers and chisels chipped boulders into gravel and fill. Their dynamite and drills thrust tunnels deep into the mountain. At night, the crew would sit around the campfire chewing tobacco, playing cards, and talking.

From one camp to another, the men trekked up the rail line, their food and tools dangling from sturdy shoulder poles. When they met other workers, Chu would run ahead and shout his father's name and ask for news. But the workers just shook their heads grimly.

"Search no more, young man!" one grizzled old worker said. "Don't you know that too many have died here? My own brother was buried alive in a mud slide."

"My uncle was killed in a dynamite blast," muttered another. "No one warned him about the fuse."

The angry memories rose and swirled like smoke among the workers.

"The white boss treats us like mules and dogs!"

"They need a railway to tie this nation together, but they can't afford to pay decent wages."

"What kind of country is this?"

Chu listened, but still he felt certain that his father was alive.

Then winter came and halted all work. Snows buried everything under a heavy blanket of white. The white boss went to town to live in a warm hotel, but Chu and the workers stayed in camp. The men tied potato sacks around their feet and huddled by the fire, while ice storms howled like wolves through the mountains. Chu thought the winter would never end.

When spring finally arrived, the survivors struggled outside and shook the chill from their bones. They dug graves for two workers who had succumbed to sickness. They watched the river surge alive from the melting snow. Work resumed, and Chu began to search again for his father.

Late one afternoon, the gang reached a mountain with a half-finished tunnel. As usual, Chu ran up to shout his father's name, but before he could say a word, other workers came running out of the tunnel.

"It's haunted!" they cried. "Watch out! There are ghosts inside!"

"Dark figures slide soundlessly through the rocks!" one man whispered. "We hear heavy footsteps approaching but never arriving. We hear sighs and groans coming from corners where no man stands."

Chu's friends dropped their packs and refused to set up camp. But the white boss rode up on his horse and shook his fist at the men. "No work, no pay!" he shouted. "Now get to work!"

Then he galloped off. The workers squatted on the rocks and looked helplessly at one another. They needed the money badly for food and supplies.

Chu stood up. "What is there to fear?" he cried. "The ghosts have no reason to harm us. There is no reason to be afraid. We have hurt no one."

"Do you want to die?" a man called out.

"I will spend the night inside the tunnel," Chu declared as the men muttered unbelievingly. "Tomorrow we can work."

Chu took his bedroll, a lamp, and food and marched into the mountain. He heard the crunch of his boots and water dripping. He knelt to light his lamp. Rocks lay in loose piles everywhere, and the shadowy walls closed in on him.

At the end of the tunnel he sat down and ate his food. He closed his eyes and wondered where his father was. He pictured his mother weeping in her bed and heard her voice calling his father's name.

Chu awoke gasping for breath. Something heavy was pressing down on his chest. He tried to raise his arms but could not. He clenched his fists and summoned all his strength, but still he was paralyzed. His eyes strained into the darkness, but saw nothing.

Suddenly the pressure eased and Chu groped for the lamp. As the chamber sprang into light, he cried, "What do you want? Who are you?"

Silence greeted him, and then a murmur sounded from behind. Chu spun around and saw a figure in the shadows. He slowly raised the lamp. The flickering light traveled up blood-stained trousers and a mud-encrusted jacket. Then Chu saw his father's face.

"Papa!" he whispered, lunging forward.

"No! Do not come closer!" The figure stopped him. "I am not of your world. Do not embrace me."

Tears rose in Chu's eyes. "So, it's true," he choked. "You . . . you have left us . . ."

His father's voice quivered with rage. "I am gone, but I am not done yet. My son, an accident here killed many men. A fuse exploded before the workers could run. A ton of rock dropped on us and crushed us flat. They buried the whites in a churchyard, but our bodies were thrown into the river, where the current swept us away. We have no final resting place."

Chu fell upon his knees. "What shall I do?"

His father's words filled the tunnel. "Take chopsticks; they shall be our bones. Take straw matting; that can be our flesh. Wrap them together and tie them tightly. Take the bundles to the mountain top high above the nests of eagles, and cover us with soil. Pour tea over our beds. Then we shall sleep in peace."

When Chu looked up, his father had vanished. He stumbled out of the tunnel and blurted the story to his friends. Immediately they prepared the bundles and sent him off with ropes and a shovel to the foot of the cliff; and Chu began to climb.

When he swung himself over the top of the cliff, he was so high up that he thought he could see the distant ocean. He dug the graves deeper than any wild animal could dig, and laid the bundles gently in the earth.

Then Chu brought his fists together above his head and bowed three times. He knelt and touched his forehead to the soil three times. In a loud clear voice he declared, "Three times I bow, three things I vow. Your pain shall stop now, your sleep shall soothe you now, and I will never forget you. Farewell."

Then, hanging onto the rope looped around a tree, Chu slid slowly back down the cliff. When he reached the bottom, he looked back and saw that the rope had turned into a giant snake that was sliding smoothly up the rock face.

"Good," he smiled to himself. "It will guard the graves well." Then he returned to the camp, where he and his fellow workers lit their lamps and headed into the tunnel. And spirits never again disturbed them, nor the long trains that came later.

The Herring Shed

JAY O'CALLAHAN

(Reading time: 20 minutes)

Jay O'Callahan is one of America's foremost storytellers, telling stories throughout the United States, Canada, Europe, and Africa. He performs his stories as monologues in concert and often works with symphony orchestras to expand the horizons of storytelling. His story, "The Herring Shed", is found in the anthology Homespun, *which includes dozens of tales from the best storytellers in North America.*

This story grew from a visit Jay O'Callahan made to Nova Scotia, where he met a blind housekeeper, Maggie Thomas, who could remember everything. As she told her stories, Jay began to fashion his, molding the details of Maggie's life into his own tale.

This is a long story to read in the first person, as Maggie talks, and will require some practice in preparing it for sharing with an audience of older children. But the story will have a powerful effect on the listeners, and they will likely want to share their feelings about it after you have read it.

Nova Scotia. World War II. This is Cape Tormentine. That's the Northumberland Strait down there and way beyond it is Prince Edward Island. It's six in the morning, spring here. All these people in the farmhouses around are up, and tonight they'll be turning on the radio to listen to the news about the war. We've all got people over there.

That's Maggie Thomas who just came out on the porch. She's fifteen. She worked in the herring shed last year, and the season's beginning again this morning — one hour from now, seven o'clock. She's the one to tell you about the herring shed.

* * *

I'm Maggie Thomas. I couldn't sleep last night. I was thinking all night about last season at the herring shed. I'll tell you and you'll know why I couldn't sleep. I got to be down there in one hour. Oh, before I tell you, that's Papa's boat. See, out in the strait with the brown and white sail. The best thing about the war is there's no gasoline so you make your own sail. I helped Papa.

Well, let me tell you about last season. As a girl of fourteen, I was very, very keen to take on the work in the herring shed. In years before, my brother Harry had worked there, but he was in the war fighting over there, so I got the job in the herring shed. At seven in the morning, I stepped into the shed — Peg to my right, Mrs. Fraser across. Peg is fifteen and she has long black braids and merry eyes, and Mrs. Fraser has the longest nose I ever saw and the nicest smile. She's my boss, a widow, Mama's age.

"Maggie?"

"Yes, Mrs. Fraser."

"Now, Maggie, I know your brother Harry worked here, but just let me explain everything. Now the great big barrel outside — that's the pickle barrel — and the herring come right down on the slides. See? They're coming down now right onto the zinc table. You get on the rubber apron. That's it. You don't want to be wet because then you'll be cold. All right. Now what you want to do is put eighteen of the herring onto the rod — it's called stringing it — and you put the rod on the rack there, and Corner Murdock will come and bring it to the drying shed. You know Corner?"

"Yes. He leaves his cows in the corner."

"That's right. Now all day he's sipping at a vanilla bottle. Gets kind of silly. Pay no attention."

"I won't."

"Fine. Now, you pick up the rod like this, put your thumb in the gill, open it up, and slip the herring right onto the rod. Now wait a minute. There's a rhythm. Thumb in the gill, open the mouth, slip it on the rod in the herring shed. Thumb in the gill, open the mouth, slip it on the rod in the herring shed. All right?"

"Yes. I can do it." I gave them a nod and I picked up a rod and began the work in the herring shed. "Thumb in the gill, open the mouth, slip it on the floor. . . . I'm sorry."

"Slow, Maggie. Slow. Slow."

"Yes. I will. Thumb in the gill, open the mouth. There, I got it on. Don't look at me. Thumb in the gill, open the mouth, slip it on. I've got it. I'm all right, Peg." Thumb in the gill, open the mouth, slip it on the rod in the herring shed. Thumb in the gill, open the mouth, I was doing the work in the herring shed. Eighteen on a rod, put the rod on the rack, pick up a rod without any slack, and go on with the work in the herring shed. Thumb in the gill, open the mouth, the hours passed by in the herring shed.

"Peg, I know we've got to do a lot for forty-five cents, but how much?"

"What you do, Maggie, is a hundred rods. That's called a bundle, and that's about forty-five cents."

"A hundred rods? That's eighteen hundred fish. It'll take me all summer."

"No it won't. You'll do a bundle in a week or so. You're fast."

"I better get a lot faster." Thumb in the gill, open the mouth, slip it on the rod in the herring shed. Thumb in the gill, open the mouth, it was getting so cold in the herring shed. The floor was dirt, the sea to our backs, and the door was opened, so Corner Murdock could pick up the racks and bring them across to the drying shed.

"Peg, I don't want to complain my first day. I can't feel my feet, my knees. Honest!"

"Well, it's almost lunch. Just dance or something. Go ahead."

"Well, I will." Thumb in the gill, open the mouth, I can't get it on the rod this way. Slip it on the rod in the herring shed. Thumb in the gill, open the mouth, oh, at last, it was noon in the herring shed.

We got outside and the sun was warm. We had a lunch of potato and a herring without its head. We talked of the war and the farms around and then went back to the cold, cold ground of the herring shed. Thumb in the gill, open the mouth, slip it on the rod in the herring shed. I finished the day, my very first day, in the herring shed.

"Thank you, Peg. Thanks, Mrs. Fraser. A quarter. Oh, thank you. I'm faster than Harry."

I ran on home, straight by the sea, glad to be free of the cold of the herring shed. Charlie Robertson's wheat was tiny and green in the evening light, a sight to be seen.

"Hello, Charlie."

Charlie Robertson is the most wonderful old farmer. He's eighty-nine, but he looks thirteen, except for the white hair. He's the kindest man. You've got to say his name right — Charlie Robertson. He's a Scotsman and proud of it.

"Charlie, you didn't have to come over."

"Well, of course I did, Maggie. You finished the day. You did a bundle."

"Oh, I didn't do a bundle, Charlie, but I did more than half a bundle. I'm faster than Harry."

"Oh, of course you're faster than Harry. No question about that."

"I was looking at your wheat. It looks good."

"Well, you know, I told you. There are wet seasons and dry seasons and good seasons. It's going to be a good season."

"I think it will. I'm going to show my mother the quarter. I'll see you later."

"Well, I hope so, Maggie."

I ran home, up the porch steps, but I didn't go in. I turned around, and I looked at the herring shed. It was my herring shed now. Not just Harry's and Mama's and everybody's. It was mine. I was going to run in and say, "Look, Mama." It's silly, but we all do it. Mama's gone blind, the way her mama did and her mama before her. They say someday I might go blind. Anyway, I knew just where Mama would be. She'd be sitting on the couch, right by the fire, kneading the bread. I opened the door very quietly. I don't know what it was. Maybe it was making the quarter. Mama's pretty and she's young, but she looks so frail.

"Mama! Open your hand."

"Maggie! You finished the day, dear. Come over. I'm so proud of you, Maggie. I know it's cold. And aren't they wonderful, Mrs. Fraser and Peg. And I suppose Corner Murdock's got his vanilla bottle. Don't tell your father. He doesn't think that's funny. All right? You can have my hand. A quarter! You're faster than your brother Harry. You take it. You're wonderful. Oh, I hear your father, Maggie. You show it to him."

Well, Papa came in and he was stringing the herring net across the room. It divided the room. He did it to mend the net. Papa doesn't frown and he doesn't smile, but I knew he was proud of me.

"Look, Papa, a quarter. I'm faster than Harry, I'm faster. No, I want you to take it, Papa. I want you to take it. I'm helping like everybody."

Well, Papa took it, and that night for a change, I did all the talking at supper. I told them about everything — about Mrs. Fraser and Peg, and Corner Murdock and his vanilla bottle. Papa didn't think that was so funny. I was eating my chicken to the rhythm. Thumb in the gill, open the mouth, slip it on the rod in the herring shed. I must have sung it fifty times for Papa. Thumb in the gill, open the mouth, slip it on the rod in the herring shed.

"Thanks, Maggie, very much. I've got hold of it now."

"You're welcome, Papa."

After supper, we did the dishes and Papa went over and snapped the radio on, and they were talking about Dunkirk, and there were so many people killed there. Papa went over and snapped it right off because that's where we thought Harry was.

I've never gone to sleep so fast in my life. I dreamed of Harry and he was far from dead. I could see him with that wild red hair, laughing at the cold in the herring shed.

At seven in the morning, I was back in the shed — Peg to my right, Mrs. Fraser across. I gave them a nod and I picked up a rod and went on with the work in the herring shed. Thumb in the gill, open the mouth, slip it on the rod in the herring shed. Eighteen on a rod, put the rod on a rack, pick up a rod without any slack, and a week went by in the herring shed.

I was going fast one day and Peg shouted, "You can do a bundle today, Maggie! Keep it up!"

"I will! I will!"

Thumb in the gill, open the mouth, slip it on the rod in the herring shed. Thumb in the gill, open the mouth. . . I did it! I did a bundle in the herring shed!

"Thank you, Mrs. Fraser. Forty-five cents. Thanks, Peg. See you later."

I was so happy and proud. And I'm glad it happened because the next day was terrible in the herring shed.

We were working away. Thumb in the gill, open the mouth, and the rector came in in his odd, shy way to the herring shed. The rector's got the worst job. He's twenty-six and never been a rector before. Whenever anyone dies in the war, the station agent gives the telegram to the rector, and it's got so no one wants to see the rector coming up the path. Well, he's sandy-haired and he leaned forward. "Maggie, could you come outside?"

And I knew my brother Harry was dead. For a moment, I couldn't move. I saw the telegram outside the shed. It was at Dunkirk.

"Thank you, Rector."

"I'm sorry, Maggie. I'm going to take you home."

"No. . . please. I don't want to go home. I'm sorry, Rector. I won't be any good to Mama like this. Let me get my feet on the ground. I would be very glad if you'd come tonight, Rector, with everybody."

And I went on with the work in the herring shed. Thumb in the gill, open the mouth, I went on with the work in the herring shed.

That night at home, the neighbors came around. Mrs. Fraser brought pie, Peg brought bread.

"Thanks, Mrs. Fraser. Come on, everybody. Sit down."

We must have had thirty people sitting in the kitchen. We just had the one kerosene lantern. People were telling funny stories and sad ones about Harry, and we were laughing and crying. All of a sudden the door opened, just about six inches.

"Mama! It's all right, Mama. It's Harry! It's Harry!"

I threw the door open and threw my arms around him. "Harry!"

"It's me, Corner Murdock, Maggie! It's Corner Murdock!"

"Oh, I'm sorry, Corner. I'm so sorry. Come on in."

Oh, I was so embarrassed. I wanted to run out into the night. Well, Mrs. Fraser took care of me, and Papa took care of Corner. Papa even gave Corner a whole bottle of vanilla. He never did that before.

I couldn't tell anyone why I did it. . . . Well, I did it because of the way Corner opened the door. Ever since my brother Harry was about eight, he opened the door six inches until everybody looked, and then he threw the door open and came in. That's what Corner had done.

I was so glad to be alone when everybody left. I went up to my room and looked out at the stars.

"Why did you take him, God? Do you need him up there?"

And for hours, I looked out into the blackness. I was looking at the strait, and I was trying to find the burning ship. For a hundred years, they say there has been a burning ship out there. They say the people won't give up until they find a port.

Charlie Robertson saw it. Mama saw it before she went blind. And Harry saw it on his birthday. Well, it wasn't there.

At seven in the morning, I was back in the shed — Peg to my right, Mrs. Fraser across. Peg held my hand and Mrs. Fraser gave me a big hug. The strange thing was that I felt so numb I just wanted to eat and sleep and work. And I went on with the work. Thumb in the gill, open the mouth, slip it on the rod in the herring shed. He lay in the ground, in the cold, cold ground, and the ground that was cold as the herring shed. Thumb in the gill, open the mouth, slip it on the rod in the herring shed. Thumb in the gill, open the mouth, the weeks went by in the herring shed. Thumb in the gill, open the mouth. . . I didn't realize it, but I was so fast one day, Peg shouted, "You can do two bundles, Maggie!"

"I will! I will!"

Thumb in the gill, open the mouth, slip it on the rod in the herring shed. Eighteen on a rod, a hundred to a bundle, forty-five cents. I did it. I did *two* bundles in the herring shed!

"Oh, thank you so much. Ninety cents, Mrs. Fraser. We'll buy a whole herd of cows. I'll see you later."

I ran on home, straight by the sea, glad to be free of the cold of the herring shed. Charlie Robertson's wheat was tall and green in the evening light, a sight to be seen.

"Hello, Charlie."

"Hello, Maggie. You were looking pretty far down there for a while. Good to see you."

"Oh, we're better. We're much better. Honest. We still wake up crying, and Mama says we'll do that for a year. Oh, Charlie, thank you for everything you and Margaret sent — all the meat and vegetables."

"Oh, listen, would've gone to rot at my place."

"They wouldn't have gone to rot, Charlie. You're wonderful. We talk about you all the time. Charlie, can I ask you something?"

"Well, I hope so Maggie. What is it?"

"Were you ever lonely when you were my age?"

"Oh, I was lonely all right, you know. I don't remember so much being fourteen and fifteen, but I was lonely. When I was

nine, ten, eleven, I had nobody to play with. I used to go outside. Who was I going to play with? Jimmy Davis's boy? Little
brat. I wouldn't play with him. I made up an imaginary friend.
Nobody could see him but me. Jimmy Scotsman. He was enormous, big shoulders. I'd come out and I'd say, 'Jimmy Scotsman, take my hand.' As soon as he took my hand, I was
nineteen, enormous."

"I want to meet someone like that, but someone real."

"Oh, you will, Maggie."

"I don't think so. Papa doesn't approve of dances. He says
I can never go to a dance."

"There are other ways of meeting someone."

"Do you think I'm pretty?"

"I think you're pretty, Maggie. I think you're pretty wonderful."

"Thank you. I'll see you later."

"Well, I hope so, Maggie."

Thumb in the gill, open the mouth, slip it on the rod in the
herring shed. The weeks passed by in the herring shed. Thumb
in the gill, open the mouth, slip it on the rod in the herring shed.

One day, I must have had a good sleep or something because
I was flyin'. By ten-thirty, I had done a bundle and Peg shouted
at me:

"Maggie, you can do three bundles today. You might never
do it again, but you can do three today."

"I will! I will!"

Thumb in the gill, open the mouth, slip it on the rod in the
herring shed.

"Peg, I'm not going to have lunch. Get a potato and stick it
in my mouth."

Thumb in the gill, open the mouth, slip it on the rod in the
herring shed. By two o'clock I could barely move, but I was
going to do three bundles today. I kept at it. Thumb in the gill,
open the mouth, slip it on the rod in the herring shed. Thumb
in the gill, open the mouth. . .I did it! I did three bundles in
the herring shed.

"Oh, I'm so proud, Mrs. Fraser. I never thought I'd do it. A
dollar thirty-five. We can buy a new farmhouse. Oh, thank you.
I'll see you later."

Well, it was a wonderful day. I felt so good. But the next morning when I got there, I was so stiff I could barely pick the rod

up. I picked it up and I felt awful giddy, so I started laughing and pretending I couldn't even get the fish on. I pretended to groan. Thumb in the gill, open the mouth. . . Well, Peg started laughing, and the two of us were laughing, pretending we couldn't get it on. Thumb in the gill, open the mouth . . . We looked at Mrs. Fraser and we were trying to make her laugh, but nothing breaks her concentration. Her hands are like fairies gone mad. Thumb in the gill, open the mouth, slip it on the rod in the herring shed. Thumb in the gill, open the mouth, slip it on the rod in the herring shed.

The two of us bent over calling, "Mrs. Fraser." We said it slow as molasses. Thumb in the gill, open the mouth. . . We saw the littlest bit of a smile, and we knew we had her. Peg picked up her black braids and pretended she was an opera star. Thumb in the gill, open the mouth . . . And I bent over with my rod. "Mrs. Fraser." Thumb in the gill, open the mouth. . . She couldn't resist us. She dropped the rod and she bent back and started laughing and clapping. And we danced around. Thumb in the gill, open the mouth, slip it on the rod in the herring shed.

We were dancing around and Corner Murdock came in. He looked like an elephant's trunk, and he bent over and picked up the drying rack, and all of a sudden, Peg got one arm, and I got the other. Thumb in the gill, open the mouth, and we danced around with him. I was dancing with a man though it was Corner. Thumb in the gill, open the mouth, slip it on the rod in the herring shed.

"All right now," Corner said wildly. "Thank you very much. That's enough."

We wouldn't let him go, and he stared at Mrs. Fraser. She picked up the rod and pretended she was conducting. Thumb in the gill, open the mouth. . . Well, poor Corner Murdock dropped the rack and ran outside, and with all watching, he opened his vanilla bottle and he drank it down. Oh, and we laughed and danced and sang, and Mrs. Fraser told stories about her grandmother. And we worked too. I made six cents that day. It was the most wonderful day of the whole summer, and it was good it was, because the next two days were the worst.

We were back to normal the next day. We were working away at ten o'clock. Thumb in the gill, open the mouth, and the rector came into the herring shed. He leaned forward in that shy way.

"Mrs. Fraser, will you come outside?" She came right around the zinc table. She wasn't going out.

"It's one of my sons, isn't it? Dead?"

"I'm sorry. It's Jack."

"Oh, God!"

She wept right in front of us, and then she straightened up and she cried, "Well, please God, if it has to be one, it should be Jack. Gannett's got a wife and a son. You know that!"

"I've got the car outside. I'll take you home."

"I'm not going home, Rector. Thank you. There's no one at home. I'll finish the way Maggie did. But I'll be very glad if you come tonight with everybody."

And she went on with the work in the herring shed. Thumb in the gill, open the mouth, the war came home to the herring shed.

I ran on home, straight by the sea, glad to be free of the cold of the herring shed.

"Hello, Charlie."

"I'm sorry, Maggie. Sad day. Is she all right?"

"She's a strong woman, Charlie. She kept working to the end. We'll see you there tonight. We'll bring the chicken."

"We'll bring the scalloped potatoes."

"See you later, Charlie."

"Well, I hope so, Maggie."

At seven in the morning, we were back in the shed — Peg to my right, Mrs. Fraser across. She came to work despite her loss, and we went on with the work in the herring shed. Thumb in the gill, open the mouth. . . The rector came in at ten o'clock, and Mrs. Fraser came right around. "Rector, very kind of you, but I'll be all right now. I've got Peg and Maggie here and at least Gannett's alive."

And the rector was still.

"Gannett's alive, isn't he?" Then she cried out, "Gannett's alive?"

"No, he's dead."

"God! Oh, God!"

And she fell to the floor in the herring shed. She was taken on home and put to bed, and we went on with the work. Thumb in the gill, open the mouth, slip it on the rod in the herring shed. We went on with the work in the herring shed. I ran on home, straight by the sea, glad to be free of the cold of the herring shed, and I swore I would never go back to the herring shed. It was too cold, and it was too sad. I'd make money, but some other way.

"Hello, Charlie. Don't want to talk, Charlie. I'll see you there tonight."

We paid Mrs. Fraser another evening call and brought food. Then we went home, and Papa turned on the radio. Mr. Churchill was speaking, and he sounded so strong. His words were old and simple and bold. "We shall never give up. We shall never give in. We shall fight on the beaches. We shall fight in the fields. We shall fight in the streets. We shall never surrender. We'll go on to the end." We sat at the table and our eyes were wet, and I looked at Papa and his fists were set. Papa stood up and then he smashed the table with his fist and cried, "Damn it, Maggie! We'll go on to the end!"

At seven in the morning, I was back in the shed — Peg to my right, and Mrs. Fraser came in. She looked so old and so thin. But she gave us a nod and she picked up the rod and went on with the work. Thumb in the gill, open the mouth, slip it on the rod in the herring shed. The herring that are dried are put on the ships and sent to England for hungry lips. We went on with the work in the herring shed. Oh, we went on, yes, we went on, dear God, we went on with the work in the herring shed. We went on with the work in the herring shed.

Well, the season finally ended, and I was so glad. I stood outside until Corner Murdock snapped the lock, and it was done.

It was harvest season. Everyone had to help, even Mrs. Fraser. You couldn't be too sad. And finally the winter came, and I'll never forget.

It snowed all day and all night, and Mama said we'd find the laughter underneath the snow. She was right. Sometimes there would be six or seven people sitting around the kitchen at night telling stories. It was fun outside, too. I built a snowman one day.

"Charlie! Charlie! Who do you think the snowman is?"

"I don't know, Maggie."

"It's you."

"Well, I thought so."

"You did not."

"Well, listen. Your father doing the cutting?"

"Well, he's cutting all right. Four cords of wood for you on

Friday."

"What about the grain?"

"He's going to bring the grain over as soon as the ice is hard. Let's have a snowball fight."

"I think I'll pass it up, Maggie."

"I'll see you later."

"Well, I hope so, Maggie."

I wanted the winter to go on forever. But it's over. You can smell the air this morning. It's spring. Oh. It must be seven o'clock. I'm going to have to hurry. That's Peg going into the herring shed. Mrs. Fraser's already there. Well, you know why I couldn't sleep. But before I go, that's Papa's boat you see down there. I told you the best thing about the war is there's no gasoline. You make your own sails. I helped Papa make those. Well, I've got to go. I'll see you later.

Thumb in the gill, open the mouth, slip it on the rod in the herring shed. Eighteen in a row, a hundred in a bundle, forty-five cents. We'll go on with the work in the herring shed.

"Hello, Mrs. Fraser. Nice to see you. Hello, Peg. Your braids look so nice. Mrs. Fraser, you'll have to tell stories again this year. Oh, I'll never be as fast as you."

The herring that are dried are put on the ships and sent to England for hungry lips. We'll go on with the work in the herring shed. Thumb in the gill, open the mouth, slip it on the rod in the herring shed. Thumb in the gill, open the mouth, that is my tale of the herring shed.

Story Sets

Each story I have included in this anthology is part of a set of stories that grows every year, connected to other works by the author or illustrator, different versions of the same tale, selections involving the same themes, or other stories that provoke similar responses in listeners.

''O W L''

From:
The Magic Orange Tree
Diane Wolkstein
(New York: Schocken Books, 1980)

All of these unusual stories throw light on the beliefs and practices of the Haitian people. Wolkstein found the tales herself on the island by listening to Haitian storytellers, and her collection is the finest of its kind.

Other books by Diane Wolkstein:
The Red Lion
White Wave

Related stories:

The Orphan Boy
Tololwa M. Mollel; illustrated by Paul Morin
(Toronto: Oxford University Press, 1990)

The author retells a beautiful Masai tale from his homeland, a story of broken trust. The illustrator travelled to Africa to bring the story to life with his pictures.

Talk that Talk: An Anthology of African-American Storytelling
Edited by Linda Gass and Marian E. Barnes
(New York: Simon & Schuster, 1989)

A comprehensive collection of 100 tales from the oral tradition of African-American folklore, told by dozens of well-known storytellers from the Caribbean, the United States, and Africa.

''WILEY AND THE HAIRY MAN''

From:
The Faber Book of North American Legends
Edited by Virginia Haviland
(New York: Pantheon House, Random House Inc., 1986)

Related stories:
The Classic Fairy Tales
Iona and Peter Opie
(London: Oxford University Press, 1974)

Twenty-four of the best-known fairy tales in the exact words in which they were first published in English, with historical introductions and a selection of fine illustrations by artists of the 19th and 20th centuries.

The Virago Book of Fairy Tales
Edited by Angela Carter
(London: Virago Press Limited, 1990)

A collection of fairy tales featuring heroines, illustrated by Corinna Sargood.

''THE PORCELAIN MAN''

From:
Richard Kennedy: Collected Stories
Richard Kennedy; illustrated by Marcia Sewell
(New York: Harper & Row, 1987)

This collection includes sixteen stories by this wonderful writer, all previously published as individual books.

Other books by Richard Kennedy:
Amy's Eyes
The Boxcar at the Center of the Universe

Related stories:

The Ghost-Eye Tree
Bill Martin Jr. and John Archambault; illustrated by Ted Rand
(New York: Henry Holt & Company, 1985)

A readers' theatre piece developed by the authors that presents a read-aloud project for parents and teachers.

Wings
Jane Yolen; illustrated by Dennis Nolan
(San Diego: Harcourt Brace Jovanovich, 1991)

Jane Yolen retells the Greek Legend of Daedalus and his son Icarus. With powerful paintings by Dennis Nolan.

Also by Jane Yolen:
Encounter

''GALLYMANDERS! GALLYMANDERS!''

From:
Grandfather Tales: American-English Folktales
Richard Chase
(Boston: Houghton Mifflin, 1948)

Richard Chase retells stories told to him by folks in North Carolina and Virginia — tall tales, folktales, versions of British fairy tales.

Related stories:
The Jack Tales: Folk Tales from the Southern Appalachians
Richard Chase
(Boston: Houghton Mifflin, 1943)

These stories of Jack were handed down for generations in the mountain country of North Carolina. You can trace these versions to the original settlers from the British Isles.

Tales of Trickery from the Land of Spoof
Alvin Schwartz; illustrated by David Christiana
(New York: Farrar, Straus & Giroux, 1985)

Alvin Schwartz adds to his series of books celebrating trickster lore, hoaxes, and folktales with twisted endings.

Other books by Alvin Schwartz:
Fat Man in a Fur Coat
Whoppers, Tall Tales and Other Lies

"HARRY-CAP AND THE THREE BROTHERS"
From:
A Bag of Moonshine
Alan Garner; illustrated by Patrick James Lynch
(London: William Collins Sons & Co. Ltd., 1986)

A collection of stories taken from the folklore of England and Wales.

Other books by Alan Garner:
Alan Garner's Book of British Fairy Tales
Fairy Tales of Gold

Related stories:

British Folktales: New Versions
Kevin Crossley-Holland
(London: Franklin Watts, Inc., 1987)

A comprehensive retelling of the great body of British folktales, from fairy tales to tales of country folk.

Other books by Kevin Crossley-Holland:
The Norse Myths
The Dead Moon

The Complete Grimms' Fairy Tales
Commentary by Joseph Campbell
(Toronto: Random House, 1972)

A classic edition of 210 tales translated by James Stern.

"THE PECULIAR SUCH THING"
From:
The People Could Fly: American Black Folktales
Virginia Hamilton; illustrated by Leo and Diane Dillon
(New York: Alfred A. Knopf, 1985)

Virginia Hamilton retells 24 selections drawn from her own black ancestry, from Brer Rabbit trickster tales to true slave narratives.

Other books by Virginia Hamilton:
In the Beginning: Creation Stories from Around the World
The Dark Way: Stories from the Spirit World
The Bells of Christmas
The Planet of Junior Brown
Sweet Whispers, Brother Rush

"THE BLUE BOTTLE"

From:
Tales for the Telling: Irish Folk and Fairy Tales
Edna O'Brien; illustrated by Michael Foreman
(London: Pavillion Books Limited, 1986)

Edna O'Brien retells these traditional Irish tales of curses, broken promises, and horses that run faster than the wind.

Related stories:

Canadian Fairy Tales
Eva Martin; illustrated by Laszlo Gal
(Vancouver: Douglas & McIntyre, 1984)

Eva Martin has collected and retold twelve Canadian fairy tales drawn from the French, Irish, and British oral traditions of the European settlers of Canada.

Seasons of Splendour: Tales, Myths and Legends of India
Madhur Jaffrey; illustrated by Michael Foreman
(London: Pavillion Books Limited, 1984)

These stories and legends of India are brought to life in the tales Madhur Jaffrey heard in her own childhood.

Naftali, the Storyteller and His Horse, Sus
Isaac Bashevis Singer; illustrated by Margot Zemach
(New York: Farrar, Straus, Giroux, 1976)

Nine stories by this celebrated author, including stories of Chelm, the city of fools, as well as autobiographical writing.

From:
The Sounds of Language: First Grade to Eighth Grade
Edited by Bill Martin, Jr.
(Texas: DHM Publishers, 1990)

In these recently reissued anthologies Bill Martin, Jr. has selected stories and poems that cry out to be read aloud to children of all ages.

Related stories:

**Impressions Teachers' Anthologies — Kindergarten
to Seventh Grade**
Edited by David Booth et al.
(Toronto: Harcourt Brace Jovanovich, 1984-1990)

A series of anthologies of stories for reading aloud, reflecting the best in children's literature from Canada, the United States, Australia, and Great Britain.

Hey! Listen to This
Edited by Jim Trelease
(New York: Penguin Books, 1992)

Forty-eight stories collected by Jim Trelease for reading aloud at home and in school.

Short and Shivery: Thirty Chilling Tales
Robert D. San Souci
(New York: Doubleday, 1987)

Retellings of international ghost stories featuring goblins, werewolves, wizards, and, of course, ghosts.

"THE NEW LEGEND OF SAM PEPPARD"

From:
Tales for an Unknown City
Edited by Dan Yashinsky
(Montreal: McGill-Queen's University Press, 1990)

Storyteller Dan Yashinsky has collected these tales from across Canada and around the world. They were all told at weekly gatherings in Toronto.

Related stories:

Pecos Bill
Steven Kellogg
(New York: William Morrow & Company, 1986)

The exploits of Pecos Bill, superhero of Texas and western pioneers. One in a series of American legends told and illustrated by Steven Kellogg.

Other books by Steven Kellogg:
Paul Bunyan
Johnny Appleseed

Cinderella Penguin or The Little Glass Flipper
Janet Perlman
(Toronto: Kids Can Press, 1992)

A Cinderella retelling featuring penguins.

"THE ORIGIN OF DEATH"

From:
Keepers of the Earth
Joseph Bruchac
(Saskatoon, Sask: Fifth House Publishers, 1985)

This collection represents several aboriginal groups in North America, including Inuit, Micmac, Mohawk, Zuni, and Hopi. Illustrated by Mohawk artist John Kahionhes Fadden.

Also by Joseph Bruchac:
Thirteen Moons on Turtle's Back

Related stories:

Tonweya and the Eagles and Other Lakota Tales
Retold by Rosebud Yellow Robe; illustrated by Jerry Pinkney
(New York: Dial Books, 1979)

The collector, a descendant of Sitting Bull and Iron Plume, preserved these oral tales she heard as a child from her father, Chief Chouncey Yellow Robe.

**The Girl Who Married a Ghost and Other Tales from the
North American Indians**
Edited by John Bierhorst
(New York: Four Winds Press, 1978)

The tales in this anthology are drawn from a collection of Indian
narratives gathered firsthand by photographer Edward S. Curtis
during the early 1900s. They are matched with his famous
photographs to make a wonderful source for reading aloud.

Other books by John Bierhorst:
In the Trail of the Wind
Black Rainbow: Legends of the Incas and Myths of Ancient Peru

The Way to Start a Day
Byrd Baylor; illustrated by Peter Parnall
(New York: Charles Scribner's Sons, 1977)

Byrd Baylor's book opens up new insights about our relation-
ship with nature and with the land.

Other books by Byrd Baylor:
The Desert Is Theirs
Hank, I'm Your Brother
Everybody Needs a Rock

''SPIRITS OF THE RAILWAY''

From:
Tales from Gold Mountain
Paul Yee; illustrated by Simon Ng
(Toronto: Groundwood, 1989)

Historian and children's author Paul Yee has created a collection of eight original stories built upon the folk stories Chinese
workers brought to Canada during the Gold Rush and the building of the CPR.

Other books by Paul Yee:
Teach Me to Fly, Skyfighter
The Curses of Third Uncle

Related stories:

The Rainbow People
Laurence Yep
(New York: Harper & Row, 1989)

The author draws on his Chinese-American past as he retells these Chinese folktales. He says that his father picked fruit in the Chinese orchards near Sacramento, and in the evening, the exhausted workers would pass the time by telling these tales.

Other books by Laurence Yep:
Child of the Owl
Dragon of the Lost Sea

Lon Po Po: A Red-Riding Hood Story from China
Ed Young
(New York: Philomel, 1989)

Ed Young was born in Tientsin, China, grew up in Shanghai, and brings his heritage to both the illustrations and the retelling of this thousand-year-old tale of Red Riding Hood. It is a perfect read-aloud, accompanied by Young's watercolors and pastels, which recall dramatic Chinese art.

Other books by Ed Young:
Yeh Shen, A Cinderella Story from China
Eyes of the Dragon (written by Margaret Leaf)

"THE HERRING SHED"

From:
Homespun: Tales from America's Favorite Storytellers
Edited by Jimmy Neil Smith
(New York: Crown Publishers, 1988)

This collection celebrates the revival of storytelling in America with a collection of the most popular stories told by the storytellers themselves, featuring Diane Wolkstein, Jackie Torrence, and Ray Hicks.

Related Stories:

The Boxing Champion
Roch Carrier; illustrated by Sheldon Cohen
(Montreal: Tundra Press, 1991)

Roch Carrier's story of his ambition as a young adolescent to be the town's boxing champion.

Also by Roch Carrier:
The Hockey Sweater

The Wretched Stone
Chris Van Allsburg
(Boston: Houghton Mifflin Company, 1991)

Chris Van Allsburg's story, accompanied by his own strong illustrations, tells the tale of a ship bedeviled by a huge, glowing rock.

Other books by Chris Van Allsburg:
Two Bad Ants
The Stranger
Jumanji
The Garden of Abdul Gasazi

Neptune Rising
Jane Yolen
(New York: Philomel Books, 1982)

Jane Yolen's powerful retellings of tales about undersea creatures include stories of selchies, mermaids, and seagods.

Other books by Jane Yolen:
The Moon Ribbon and Other Tales
The Girl Who Cried Flowers

Acknowledgements

"The Blue Bottle" from *Tales for The Telling* by Edna O'Brien. Reprinted by permission of Pavilion Books.

"Gallymanders! Gallymanders!" from *The Grandfather Tales* by Richard Chase. Copyright 1948, © renewed 1976 by Richard Chase. Reprinted by permission of Houghton Mifflin Company.

"Harry Cap and The Three Brothers" from *A Bag of Moonshine* by Alan Garner, Harper Collins Publishers Limited.

"The Herring Shed" by Jay O'Callahan. Reprinted by permission of the author.

"The New Legend of Sam Peppard" by Celia Lottridge. Reprinted by permission of the author. First published in *Tales for an Unknown City*, Dan Yashinsky (ed.) McGill-Queens University Press, 1990.

"The Origin of Death". Reprinted by permission from *The Native Stories from Keepers of the Earth* by Joseph Bruchac. Fifth House Publishers, 1991.

"Owl" from *The Magic Orange Tree and other Haitian Folktales*, collected by Diane Wolkstein. Text copyright © 1978 by Diane Wolkstein. Reprinted by permission of Alfred A. Knopf, Inc.

"The Peculiar Such Thing" from *The People Could Fly: American Folktales* told by Virginia Hamilton. Text copyright © 1985 by Virginia Hamilton. Reprinted by permission of Alfred A. Knopf, Inc.

"The Porcelain Man" by Richard Kennedy. Reprinted by permission of the author.

"The Snake-bit Hoe Handle" by Doc McConnell. Reprinted by permission of the author. First published in *Homespun*. Edited by Jimmy Neil Smith, Crown Publishers Inc., 1988.

"Spirits of the Railway" from *Tales from Gold Mountain* by Paul Yee. Text copyright © 1989 by Paul Yee. A Groundwood Book/Douglas & MacIntyre.

Every effort has been made to acknowledge all sources of material used in this book. The publishers would be grateful if any errors or omissions were pointed out, so that they may be corrected.